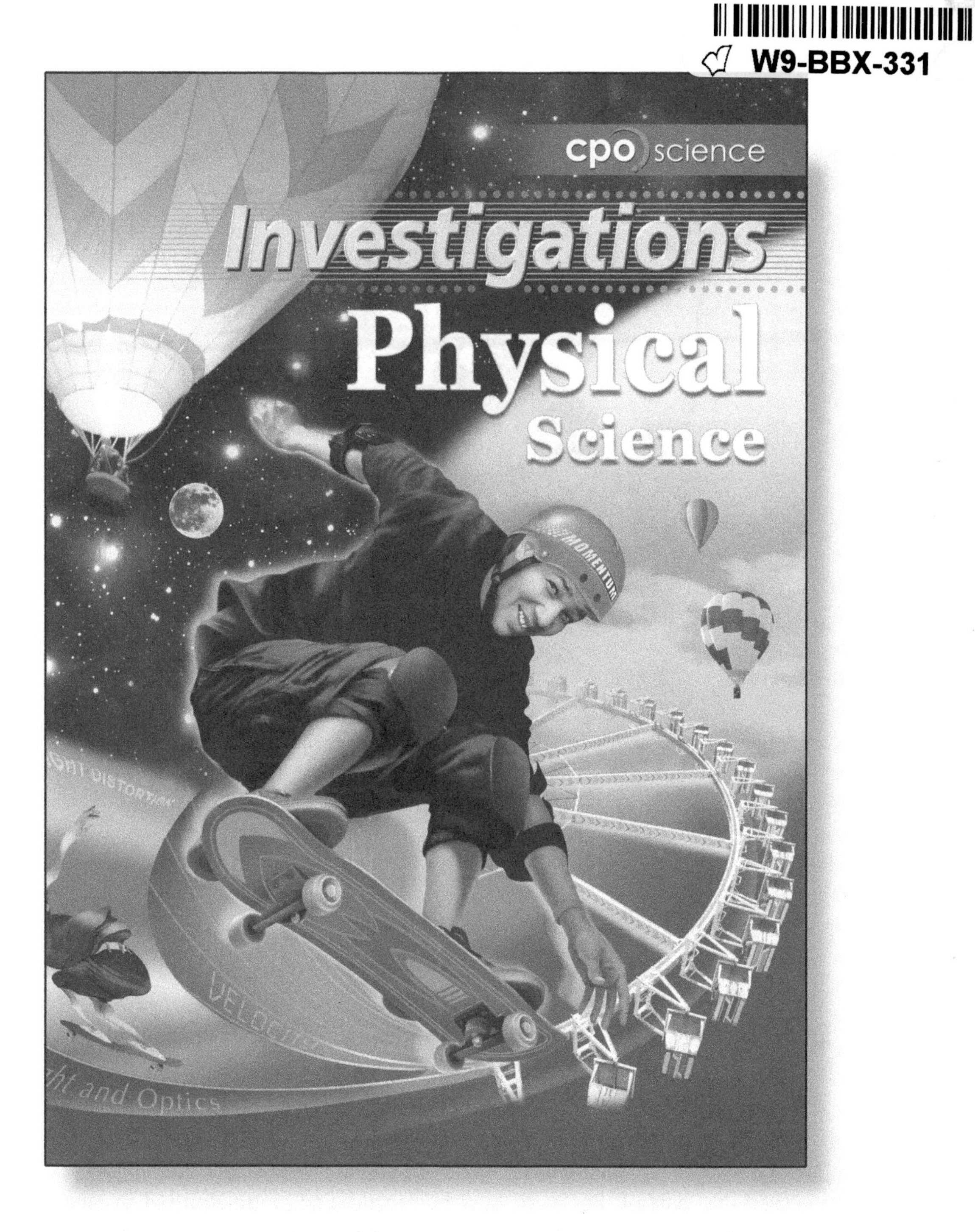
cpo science
Investigations
Physical
Science
MOMENTUM
VELOCITY
ght and Optics

cpo science
A member of
School Specialty
Science

CPO Science Physical Science Investigations
First Edition

ISBN: 978-1-58892-499-5
Part Number 492-3670
Printing 4—August, 2015
Printed by Courier, Kendallville

CPO Science
80 Northwest Boulevard
Nashua, NH 03063
(800) 932-5227
http://www. cposcience.com

Printed and Bound in the United States of America

CPO Science Staff

Thomas C. Hsu, PH.D – Author

Nationally recognized innovator in science and math education and the founder of CPO Science. He holds a Ph.D. in Applied Plasma Physics from the Massachusetts Institute of Technology (MIT), and has taught students from elementary, secondary and college levels across the nation. Tom has worked with more than 12,000 K-12 teachers and administrators and is well known as a consultant, workshop leader and developer of curriculum and equipment for inquiry based learning in science and math.

Patsy Eldridge - Principal Writer

M.ED in Education from Tufts University and a B.S in Biology from Grove City College.

As an adjunct professor for Endicott College in Beverly, Massachusetts and the College of Charleston in Charleston, South Carolina, she developed physical science courses for pre- and in-service educators. Patsy's background is in medical device research and development. She is a national inquiry-based science education consultant and presenter. Patsy has more than ten years of high school science teaching experience, and she has helped developed all of the CPO Science teaching and learning systems to date.

Erik Benton - Principal Investigation Editor

B.F.A., University of Massachusetts his minor was in Physics

Principal Investigation editor for CPO Science. Erik taught for 8 years in public and private schools, focusing on inquiry and experiential learning.

Stacy Kissel - Principal Writer

B.S., Civil and Environmental Engineering, Carnegie Mellon University; M.Ed., Physics Education, Boston College

Stacy has nine years teaching experience in physics, math and integrated science at Brookline High in Massachusetts. Stacy has been a curriculum developer with CPO for the last five years.

Scott Eddleman - Contributing Writer

B.S., Biology, Southern Illinois University; M.Ed., Harvard University

Taught for 13 years in urban and rural settings. Developed two successful science-based school-to-career programs. Nationally recognized teacher trainer in inquiry-based and project-based instruction. Participated in a fellowship at Brown University where he conducted research on the coral reefs of Belize. Worked on National Science Foundation-funded projects at TERC. Scott has been a principal writer and curriculum developer for CPO Science for the last six years.

Mary Beth Abel Hughes - Contributing Writer

B.S., Marine Biology, College of Charleston; M.S., Biological Sciences, University of Rhode Island

Mary Beth has taught a range of science and math at an innovative high school and at the college level. Her expertise is in scientific research, inquiry-based teaching methods, and curriculum development. Mary Beth has been a principal writer with CPO Science for six years.

Senior Editor

Lynda Pennell - Executive Vice President

B.A., English, M.Ed., Administration, Reading Disabilities, Northeastern University; CAGS Media, University of Massachusetts, Boston

Nationally known in high school restructuring and for integrating academic and career education. Served as the director of an urban school for 5 years and has 17 years teaching/administrative experience. In the Boston Public Schools. Lynda has led the development for CPO Science for the last six years.

Editorial Consultants

Christine Golden

Chris has been the Project Manger for *Imperial Communications* since 1999 and in the publishing business for 22 years. She is now managing editor and owner of *Big Dog Publishing* Services. Christine's work centers around the editing of K-12 textbook materials.

Reviewers

Pamella Ferris

Physics Teacher
Evans High School, Evans, GA

Brian E. Goodrow

Physical science teacher
Apple Valley Middle School, Apple Valley, CA

Sylvia Gutman

Science teacher, department chairwoman
David A. Brown Middle School
Wildomar, CA Lake Elsinore Unified School District

Tony Heinzman
Science teacher
Apple Valley Middle School, Apple Valley, CA

Philip L. Hunter

Science department chairman
Johnson Middle School, Westminster, CA

Nancy Joplin

English-language arts department chairwoman
Ray Wiltsey Middle School, Ontario, CA

Brad Joplin

Science teacher
Ray Wiltsey Middle School, Ontario, CA

Margaret J. Kilroy

Chemistry Teacher
Cartersville High School, Cartersville, GA

Dakhine Lee

Special Education Department Chair
Lewis Fraiser Middle School, Hinesville, GA

Jason C. Lee

Science Teacher
Long County High School, Ludowici, GA

Mark Matthews

Physics and Chemistry Teacher
Union Grove High School, McDonough, GA

Kelly McAllister

Science teacher
Gage Middle School, Riverside, CA

Bianca N. McRae

Science teacher, department chairwoman
Menifee Valley Middle School, Menifee, CA

Jodye Selco, Ph.D.

Professor, Center for Education and Equity in Math, Science, and Technology
California State Polytechnic University, Pomona, CA

Tia L. Shields

Life science/health and English language learning teacher
Nicolas Junior High School, Fullerton, CA

Sharon Strefling

Science Teacher
Camden County High School, Kingsland, GA

Robert M. Strong

6th Grade Language Arts Teacher
Union Grove Middle School, McDonough, GA

Illustration/Design

Polly Crisman -Designer and Illustrator

B.F.A., University of New Hampshire

Graphic artist with expertise in advertising and marketing design, freelance illustrating, and caricature art.

Bruce Holloway - Cover Designs

Pratt Institute, N.Y.; Boston Museum School of Fine Arts

Expertise in product design, advertising, and three-dimensional exhibit design. Commissioned for the New Hampshire Duck Stamp for 1999 and 2003.

Jesse Van Valkenburgh - Illustrator

Graduated from the Rochester Institute of Technology with a B.A. in Illustration.

Jesse has worked in prepress and design responsible for creative design and prepress film production. Jesse also worked at PC Connection as a graphic designer for catalog and direct mailing design, logo design, as well as some illustration work.

James Travers - Graphic Designer and Animator

Associate's degree of Applied Business and Commercial Art, Akron University

Has held positions as graphic designer, art development manager, and currently is a commissioned artist.

Equipment Design and Material Support

Thomas C. Hsu, Ph.D

Ph.D. in Applied Plasma Physics from the Massachusetts Institute of Technology

Tom is a nationally recognized innovator in science and math education and the founder of CPO Science. Well known as a consultant, workshop leader and developer of curriculum and equipment for inquiry based learning in science and math.

Thomas Narro - Senior Vice President

B.S., Mechanical Engineering, Rensselaer Polytechnic Institute

Thomas is an accomplished design and manufacturing engineer and experienced consultant in corporate reengineering and industrial-environmental acoustics.

Material Support

Kathryn Gavin - Purchasing and Quality Control Manager

Kathryn is responsible for all functions related to purchasing raw materials and quality control of finished goods. She works closely with product development and design.

Lisa LaChance - Senior Materials Specialist

Associate's of Science in Accounting

Lisa evaluates material samples to ensure materials meet project requirements. She develops and manages the release of materials specifications.

Technical Support

Tracy Morrow

B.A., English, Texas A&M University; M.A., English, Sam Houston State University, TX

Tracy taught middle school in Klein ISD, a suburb of Houston, Texas, for 9 years preparatory and English at Tomball College for 5 years. Tracy worked as a technical writer in the oil and gas, airlines, and real estate industries. Currently she offers consulting services and technical training. Tracy's expertise lies in the editing program Framemaker.

How to Read an Investigation

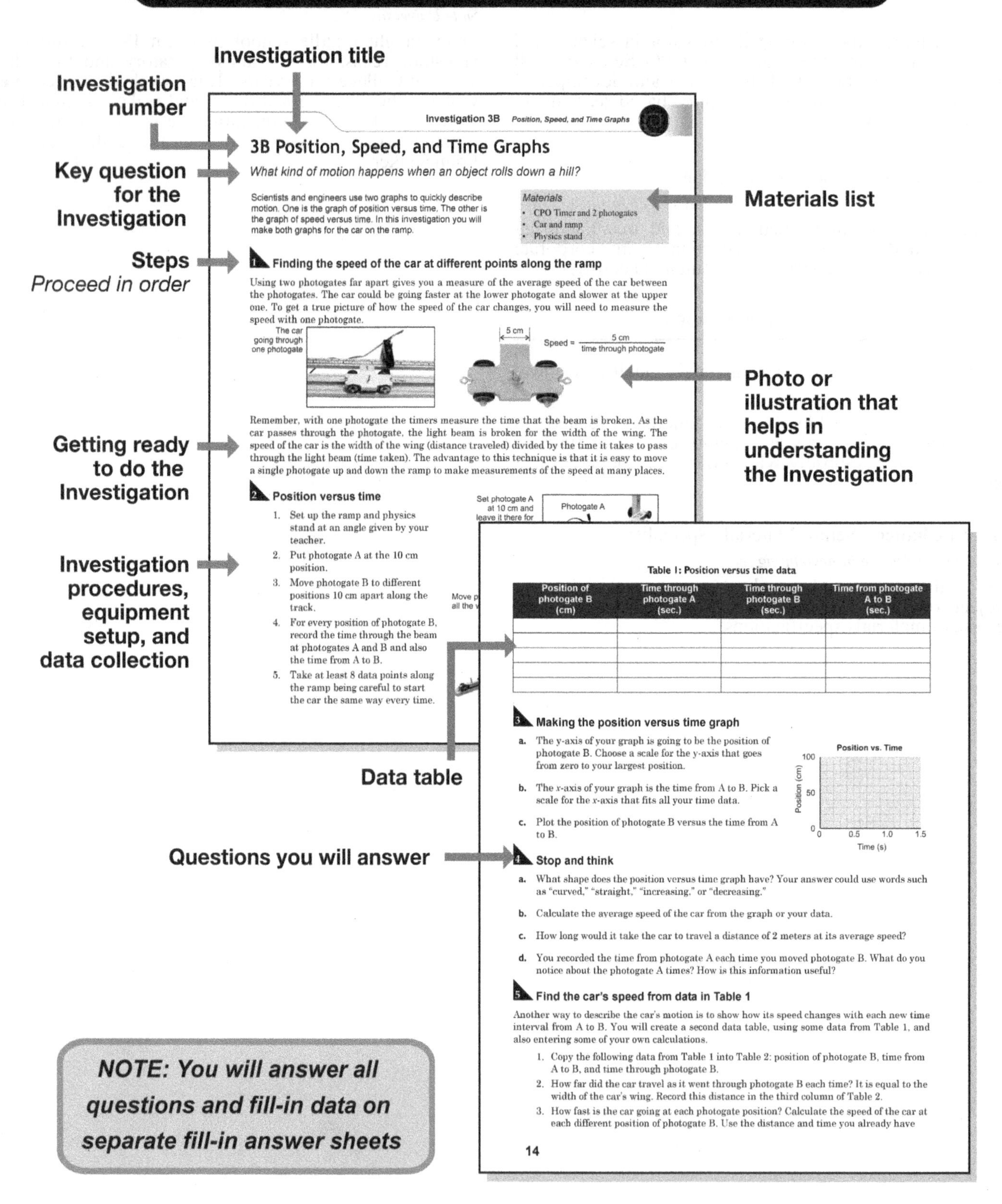

Investigation 3B *Position, Speed, and Time Graphs*

3B Position, Speed, and Time Graphs

What kind of motion happens when an object rolls down a hill?

Scientists and engineers use two graphs to quickly describe motion. One is the graph of position versus time. The other is the graph of speed versus time. In this investigation you will make both graphs for the car on the ramp.

Materials
- CPO Timer and 2 photogates
- Car and ramp
- Physics stand

1 Finding the speed of the car at different points along the ramp

Using two photogates far apart gives you a measure of the average speed of the car between the photogates. The car could be going faster at the lower photogate and slower at the upper one. To get a true picture of how the speed of the car changes, you will need to measure the speed with one photogate.

The car going through one photogate

5 cm

Speed = 5 cm / time through photogate

Remember, with one photogate the timers measure the time that the beam is broken. As the car passes through the photogate, the light beam is broken for the width of the wing. The speed of the car is the width of the wing (distance traveled) divided by the time it takes to pass through the light beam (time taken). The advantage to this technique is that it is easy to move a single photogate up and down the ramp to make measurements of the speed at many places.

2 Position versus time

1. Set up the ramp and physics stand at an angle given by your teacher.
2. Put photogate A at the 10 cm position.
3. Move photogate B to different positions 10 cm apart along the track.
4. For every position of photogate B, record the time through the beam at photogates A and B and also the time from A to B.
5. Take at least 8 data points along the ramp being careful to start the car the same way every time.

Set photogate A at 10 cm and leave it there for

Photogate A

Move p all the v

Table 1: Position versus time data

Position of photogate B (cm)	Time through photogate A (sec.)	Time through photogate B (sec.)	Time from photogate A to B (sec.)

3 Making the position versus time graph

a. The y-axis of your graph is going to be the position of photogate B. Choose a scale for the y-axis that goes from zero to your largest position.

b. The x-axis of your graph is the time from A to B. Pick a scale for the x-axis that fits all your time data.

c. Plot the position of photogate B versus the time from A to B.

Position vs. Time
Position (cm): 0, 50, 100
Time (s): 0, 0.5, 1.0, 1.5

4 Stop and think

a. What shape does the position versus time graph have? Your answer could use words such as "curved," "straight," "increasing," or "decreasing."

b. Calculate the average speed of the car from the graph or your data.

c. How long would it take the car to travel a distance of 2 meters at its average speed?

d. You recorded the time from photogate A each time you moved photogate B. What do you notice about the photogate A times? How is this information useful?

5 Find the car's speed from data in Table 1

Another way to describe the car's motion is to show how its speed changes with each new time interval from A to B. You will create a second data table, using some data from Table 1, and also entering some of your own calculations.

1. Copy the following data from Table 1 into Table 2: position of photogate B, time from A to B, and time through photogate B.
2. How far did the car travel as it went through photogate B each time? It is equal to the width of the car's wing. Record this distance in the third column of Table 2.
3. How fast is the car going at each photogate position? Calculate the speed of the car at each different position of photogate B. Use the distance and time you already have

14

Table of Contents

Additional Materials

1A Measuring Time

How is time measured accurately?

A measurement is a quantity with a unit that tells what the quantity means. For example, 3 seconds is a measurement of time that includes a quantity (3) and a unit (seconds). This investigation will explore time measurement.

Materials

- CPO Timer and 2 photogates.

1 Using the timer as a stopwatch

A stopwatch measures a **time interval**. The stopwatch is started and stopped with the "**A**" button. The display shows time in seconds up to 60 seconds. The display shows **min:sec** for times longer than one minute.

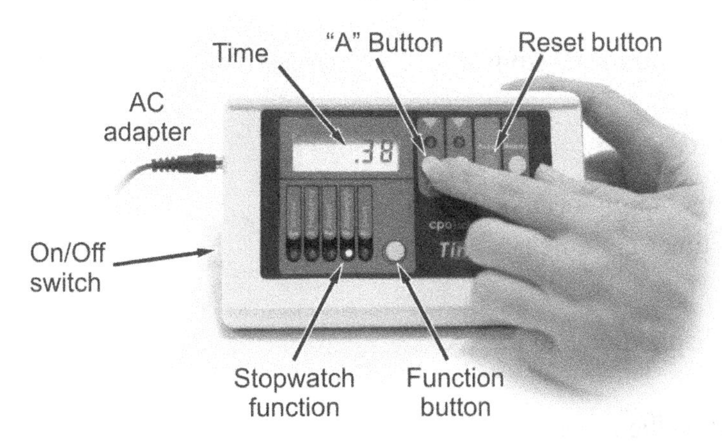

1. The timer has different functions. The first one to try is **stopwatch**. Set the timer to **stopwatch** using the function button.
2. Start and stop the timer with the "**A**" button.
3. Reset the stopwatch to zero with the reset (**O**) button.

2 Observing reaction time

The time it takes a signal from your brain to move a muscle is called **reaction time**.

1. This experiment takes two people. One person (the watcher) watches the stopwatch and the other person pushes the buttons. The watcher should think of a number between 5 and 10 seconds and keep the number secret.
2. The second person starts (and stops) the stopwatch *without looking at the display.* The watcher looks at the display and says STOP at the secret number. For example, if the secret number is 6 the watcher should say STOP when the display reaches 6.00 seconds.
3. Repeat the experiment several times and estimate reaction time.

3 Mixed units for time

In physical science, you are usually going to measure time in seconds. However, time is often given in mixed units, which may include hours, minutes, and seconds. Consider the following three time intervals.

1. 16,000 seconds
2. 250 minutes
3. 4 hours, 23 minutes and 15 seconds (4:23:15)

a. Which one is in mixed units?

b. Can you tell which time is longest or shortest?

c. If 1 minute = 60 seconds, then how many seconds is 250 minutes?

d. If 1 hour = 60 minutes, then how many minutes are in 4 hours?

e. Use part (d) to figure out how many seconds are in 4:23:15.

f. Arrange the three measurements from smallest to largest:

4 Using the photogates

A photogate allows us to use a light beam to start and stop the timer. When the timer is in interval mode, it uses photogates to control the clock.

1. Connect a single photogate to the "**A**" input with a cord.
2. Select **interval** on the timer.
3. Push the "**A**" button and the "**A**" light should come on and stay on.
4. Try blocking the light beam with your finger and observe what happens to the timer.

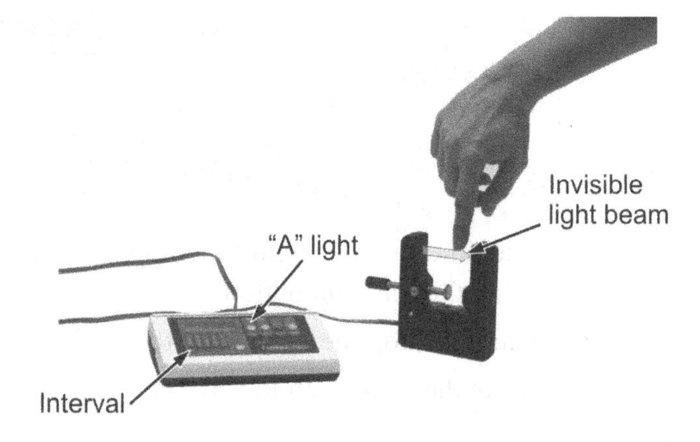

Try your own experiments until you can answer the following questions. Be very specific in your answer. Someone who has never used the timer before should be able to read your answer and know what to do with the light beam to make the clock start and stop.

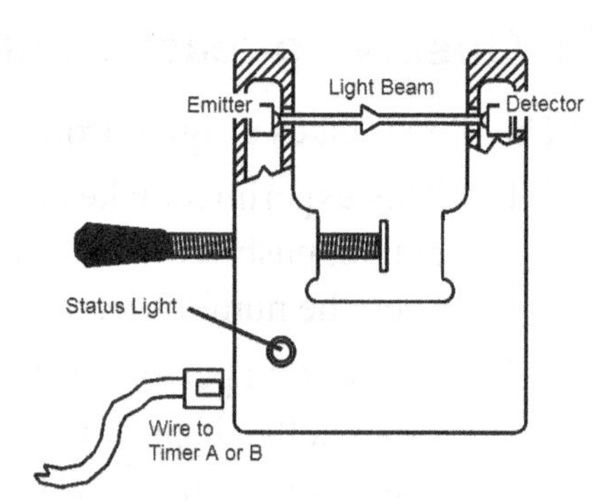

a. How do you start the clock?

b. How do you stop the clock?

c. What time interval has the clock measured?

5 Using the timer with two photogates

1. Connect a second photogate to the socket behind the B button (input B). You should now have two photogates connected to the timer.
2. Make sure the light on each photogate is green and press the reset button. Pressing reset clears the clocks and also tells the timer to look at its inputs to see which photogates are connected.
3. Use the A and B buttons to turn the A and B lights on and off. The timer does something slightly different for each combination of lights shown in Table 1.
4. Do your own experiments and fill in the rest of Table 1.

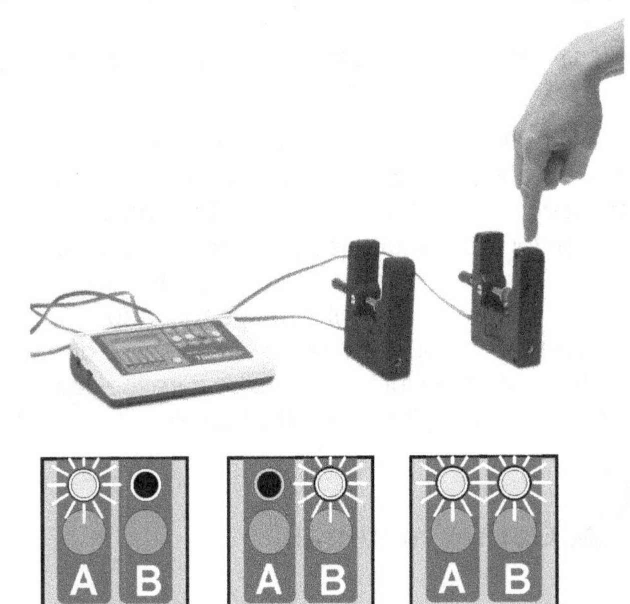

What starts and stops the displayed time for each setting of the A and B lights?

A light	B light	How do you start the clock?	How do you stop the clock?	What time interval does the timer display?
On	Off			
Off	On			
On	On			
Off	Off			

Try this; Turn the A and B lights off. Pass a finger through photogate A and then photogate B.

a. Turn the A light on. What is displayed on the timer?

b. Turn the A light off, and then turn the B light on. What is displayed?

c. Turn both A and B lights on. What is displayed? What does this tell you about the timer?

6 Another test to try

Set the timer up with one photogate in input A. Turn the A light on and pass your finger back and forth through the light beam. Do it fast and also do it very slowly. Answer the following questions based on what you see.

a. Do the times add up or do they start again from zero each time your finger breaks the beam?

b. Suppose the times added. What should happen to the time on the display as you keep passing your finger back and forth through the light beam?

c. How does your answer to (6b) affect your answer to (6a)?

1B Measuring Mass and Length

How do scientists measure mass and length?

Mass and length are common properties to measure in physical science. Suppose you had to design a strong case to protect a laptop computer. You would need to find the mass of different materials, so you could choose one that is not too heavy but strong enough to protect the laptop. You would also need to do a lot of length measurements, to be sure the case was large enough to carry the laptop.

Materials

- 1 large square metal washer
- 100 mL water
- 1 pencil
- 10 paperclips (chained together)
- 4 round washers (1/2 inch inner diameter works well)
- Electronic scale (or triple beam balance)
- Metric ruler

1 Gather materials

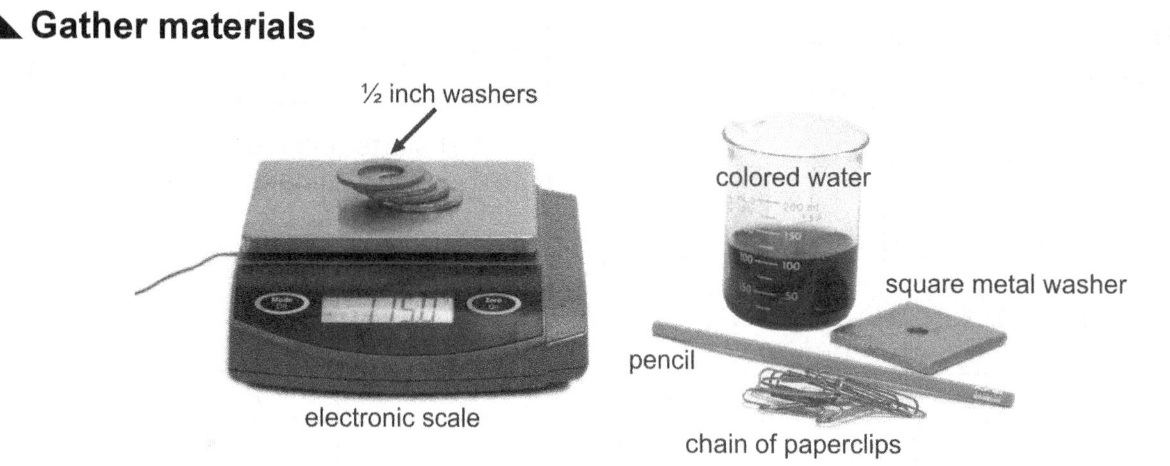

2 Measuring Mass

Mass is the amount of matter in an object. A common metric unit of mass for small objects is the gram (g).

1. Place each object listed in the table on your electronic scale (or triple beam balance). Record the mass in grams.
2. Hint: when you find the mass of the water, how will you exclude the mass of the beaker?

Table 1: Mass in Grams

Object	Mass (g)
1 large square metal washer	
1 pencil	
Chain of 10 paperclips	
4 round washers	
100 mL water	

3 Analyzing your results

How do your mass measurements compare with other groups' measurements? Create a class data table that shows each group's mass measurement for the pencil.

a. Did every group record the same mass for the pencil? List possible reasons for differences.

b. Choose one particular pencil. If each group found the mass of the same pencil, would the measurements all be the same? Try it and explain the results.

c. What happens to the mass if you sharpen the pencil? Try it and explain your results.

d. You found the mass of a chain of ten paperclips. Without using your scale, how could you estimate the mass of ONE paperclip? Explain your method, estimate the mass, and then measure one paper clip. How does the actual mass compare to your estimate?

4 Measuring length

The centimeter (cm) is a common metric unit used to measure the dimensions of small classroom objects. Use a metric ruler to measure the objects described in Table 2.

centimeter side of ruler

Table 2: Measuring Length

Object	Length (cm)
Square weight	
Pencil	
10 paperclips	
round washer	

5 Analyzing your results

How does your group's data compare with other groups' measurements? Create a class data table that shows each group's measurement for the large square metal washer and the chain of paperclips.

a. Did every group record the same length for the square metal washer? What are some reasons for differences?

b. Did every group record the same length for the chain of paperclips? What could account for differences?

6 Thinking about what you observed

a. You made measurements with an electronic scale and a metric ruler. Which device would you consider to be the most reliable? Explain your choice.

b. Suppose you have to teach a young child to use a metric ruler to measure an object. Describe the step-by-step technique you would use to help the child make an accurate measurement.

2A Inquiry and Scientific Evidence

How does a scientist conduct investigations?

This investigation is about solving a scientific mystery using the same processes that scientists use to discover new things. The mystery is the identity of the object in the box. You have to determine which clay shape you have in your box without opening the box. Your teacher will give your group a box with an unknown clay shape (one of the four) sealed inside.

Materials

- A small box with a clay shape sealed inside

1 Setting up

1. Your teacher will give you a small box that has a clay shape sealed inside.
2. The clay shapes started as ping-pong-ball sized pieces. Your teacher (or a student helper) created four different clay shapes: a sphere, cube, cylinder, and cone. Your box has one of these shapes inside.

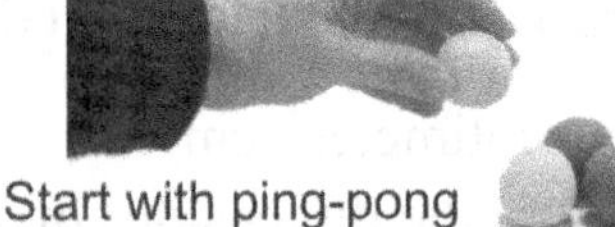

Start with ping-pong ball sized pieces of clay

2 Stop and think

a. Write down at least one thing you know about each clay object. How would the shapes roll? How would they sound when you shake the box?

b. Write down at least 3 different observations you could make that might help you figure out which shape is inside a closed box. Assume you can hold the box and do anything (in your classroom) except open it or damage the box or contents in any way.

3 Conducting your inquiry

Try doing the things you suggested in part 2b above. Write down the results as carefully as you can.

Table 1: Results of your inquiry

What you did	What you observed (evidence)

4 Your hypothesis

A hypothesis is a possible explanation. At the start of the inquiry your hypothesis is an educated guess at what shape is in the box. It may be the correct shape, but your hypothesis should fit with at least some of the observations you have made so far. Use the following questions to help write down your first hypothesis.

a. What do you think is in the box? (your hypothesis)

b. What specific things (evidence) did you observe that makes you think this hypothesis may be right?

c. Were there things that you did NOT observe which also cause you to think your hypothesis might be correct? These kinds of observation are evidence too.

5 Testing your hypothesis

As part of the scientific method, all hypotheses must be testable. That means the hypothesis must make a prediction that can be tested with an experiment. For example, suppose your hypothesis is that the clay shape in your box is a cube. You might predict that when you tip the box, the object will sound like it slides rather than rolls in the box. This is a prediction that can be tested.

a. Assume your hypothesis is right. Write down one additional test you could make to confirm that you do indeed have the right object. This test should be something you have not done before.

b. Do the test and write down what you observe.

c. Try any other ways that you can think of to examine the box.

6 Stop and think

A correct hypothesis agrees with ALL of the observations. If the hypothesis disagrees with even one observation, it cannot be completely correct.

a. Write down your hypothesis for what is in the box based on all your observations.

b. Write down at least four observations (evidence) that you made.

c. Next to each observation, write down whether it supports or does not support your hypothesis.

d. Open your box. Was your hypothesis right? If not, is there another test you could suggest that might have provided a clue to the correct hypothesis?

7 Exploring on your own

Go home and make your own mystery box using things you find around the house. The box should contain at most three objects but may contain only one. Write down at least four tests that would allow someone to solve your mystery.

2B Speed

Which ramp is fastest?

We do experiments to collect evidence that allows us to take a look at nature's mysteries. If an experiment is well planned, the results of the experiment can answer a question about how nature works. This investigation will look at the relationship between speed and angle for a car rolling down hill.

Materials

- Car and Ramp
- CPO Timer and photogates
- Physics Stand

Speed describes how fast or slow something moves. You have to put two quantities together to describe your speed: the distance you traveled, and the time it took you to go that distance. An average walking speed is 1 m/s, or 100 cm/s. What is the average speed of the car as it rolls down the ramp?

1 Set up your car and ramp

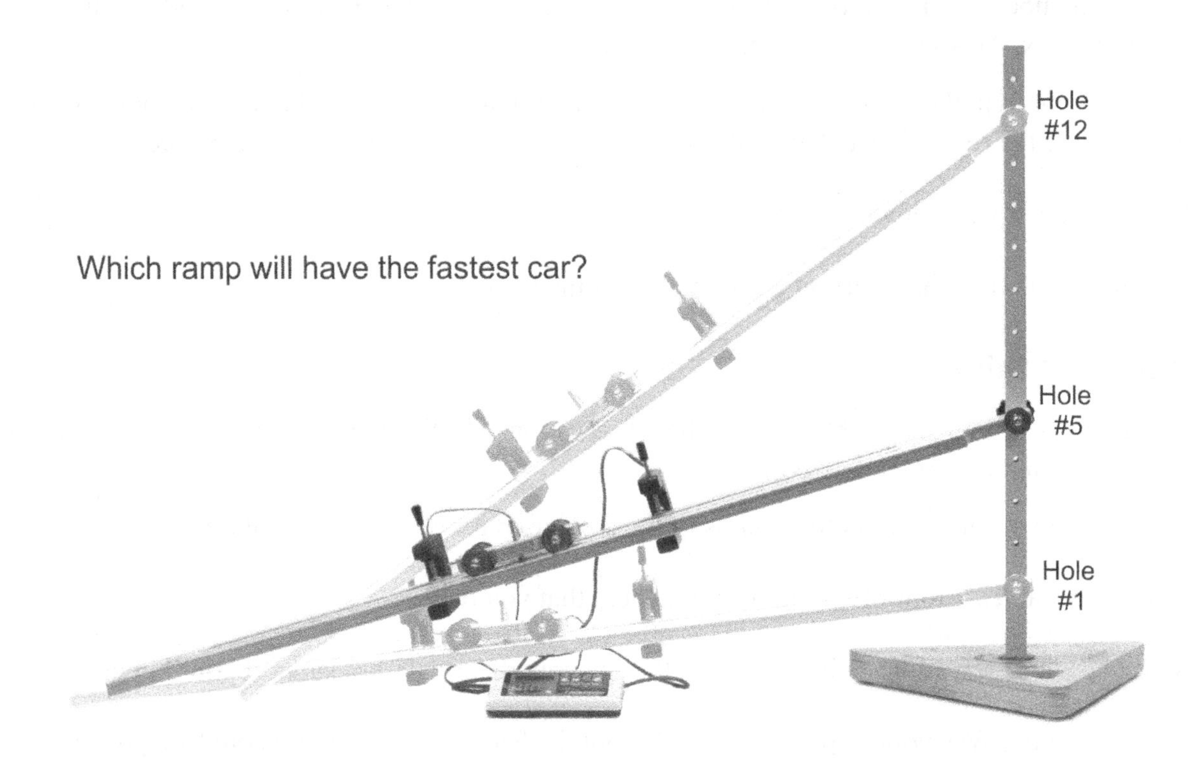

1. Set up the car and ramp as instructed by your teacher. Each group will put the ramp in a different hole of the physics stand. This means each group will have a different ramp angle.
2. To find the speed of the car, you need to know two things: the distance traveled, and the time it takes the car to go that distance. Put two photogates on the ramp so you can find how long it takes the car to go from one photogate to the other.

2 Your hypothesis

a. Look around at the other groups and compare the ramp angles.

b. Write your hypothesis, stating which ramp will have the fastest car. Explain the reasoning behind your hypothesis.

3 Find the speed of the car

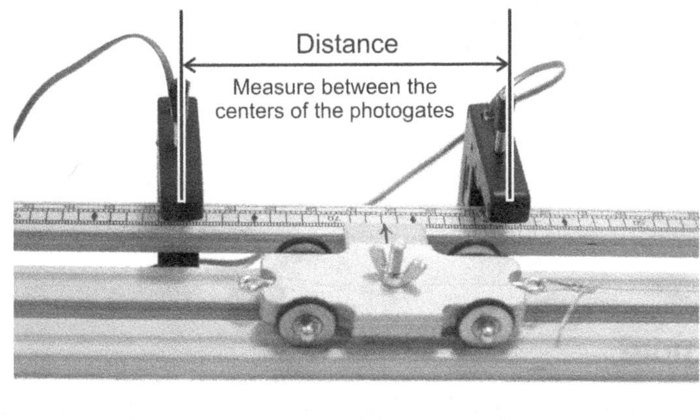

$$\text{Speed} = \frac{\text{Distance between A and B}}{\text{Time from A to B}}$$

1. Record the distance between the two photogates.
2. Roll the car down the ramp and record the time it takes to go from photogate A to B. Be sure to read the timer when the A and B lights are both on!
3. Find the average speed by dividing distance by time (speed = distance/time).
4. Do two more trials so you have a total of three trials. Find the average speed from your three trials.

Table 1: Speed of the Car

Trial	Distance A to B (cm)	Time A to B (s)	Average Speed (cm/s)
1			
2			
3			
Average Speed of the Car (cm/s)			

4 Analyzing your results

a. Create a class data table that shows the average speed for each different ramp position.

b. Do the groups' speeds agree with your hypothesis about which ramp should have the fastest car? Why or why not?

5 Design a better experiment

It was hard to compare results in the first experiment, because there were many differences in the car and ramp setups from group to group. Other variables (besides the ramp angle) changed, making it hard to compare results. A better experiment would make every variable the same except the one variable you are testing.

a. There are five major variables other than ramp angle that need to be kept the same from group to group. Discuss these variables and decide as a class how you will control each.

Table 2: Creating a Controlled Experiment

Variable	How we will control it

6 A better experiment

1. Repeat the first experiment, except this time be sure to control all variables other than ramp angle. Each group will still have a different ramp angle.

Table 3: Speed of the Car - A Controlled Experiment

Trial	Distance A to B (cm)	Time A to B (s)	Average Speed (cm/s)
1			
2			
3			
Average Speed of the Car (cm/s)			

7 Analyzing your results

a. Create a class data table that shows the average speed for each different ramp position.

b. Do the groups' speeds agree with your hypothesis about which ramp should have the fastest car? Why or why not?

c. How does your car's speed compare to an average walking speed of 1 m/s?

8 Exploring on your own

a. Which is faster — the average speed of a tsunami, or the top speed of a cheetah? Do some research to find the answer. Record the speeds you find — don't forget to include the units, and make sure you compare units that are the same!

b. Many Olympic sprinters can run 100 meters (10,000 cm) in 10 seconds. Figure out what the speed is in centimeters per second (cm/s). How does this compare to the speed of your car in the last experiment?

3A Positive and Negative Position

How do we measure position in two dimensions?

We often use positive and negative numbers to tell right and left or forward and backward. In this investigation you will be measuring distances in two dimensions around your classroom.

Materials

- Meter stick
- Index cards with directions and questions prepared in advance

1 Describing direction in two dimensions

Your *position* is your location compared to a starting point or *origin*. The origin can be any point you choose. For example, when giving the position of your school, you may choose your house to be the origin. The position of your school might be 2 kilometers east of your house. When specifying a position, both the distance and the direction must be given.

The compass directions north, south, east and west can be used to tell direction. Positive and negative x and y-coordinates can also be used to give directions. The x-coordinate tells the east-west position. East is in the positive direction, and west is in the negative direction. The y-coordinate tells the north-south position. North is in the positive direction, and south is in the negative direction. Coordinates can be written as an ordered pair (x,y).

For example, suppose the grocery store is 2 km east and 1 km south of your house. You would specify the position of the grocery store as (+2, -1) km.

2 Classroom scavenger hunt

1. Look around the floor of your classroom and locate the pieces of tape marked A, B, C, etc. Each of these letters will be used as an origin from which you will make measurements. The front of your classroom will correspond to north or +y direction.
2. Your teacher has a pile of index cards that correspond to the letters. Each index card has a letter on one side and instructions on the other side. Choose one of the index cards. Find the card's letter on the floor of your classroom.
3. Read the instructions on the card. The instructions will tell you the distance and direction you must walk from the origin. Once you reach the final position, answer the question on the card. Write your answer in Table 1.

Origin point	Answer to question
A	
B	
C	
D	
E	
F	

4. Return the index card and choose another one. Complete cards A through F.

3 Thinking about position

a. Which compass direction corresponds with the positive x direction?

b. Which compass direction corresponds with the negative y direction?

c. Which compass direction corresponds with the negative x direction?

d. Which compass direction corresponds with the positive y direction?

e. You start at the origin and walk 3 meters north and 5 meters west. What are your coordinates in (x,y) form?

f. You start at the origin and walk 2 meters south and 1 meter east. What are your coordinates in (x,y) form?

g. How would you walk to get to the position (-1,-4)m?

h. How would you walk to get to the position (+2,-5)m?

4 Making your own scavenger hunt

1. Choose one of the lettered points in the classroom as your origin. Make a scavenger hunt card that gives directions from the origin to a destination in the classroom. Write a question to be answered at your destination.
2. Trade scavenger hunt cards with another group. Follow their directions and answer the question at the destination.

3B Position, Speed, and Time Graphs

What kind of motion happens when an object rolls down a hill?

Scientists and engineers use two graphs to quickly describe motion. One is the graph of position versus time. The other is the graph of speed versus time. In this investigation you will make both graphs for the car on the ramp.

Materials

- CPO Timer and 2 photogates
- Car and Ramp
- Physics Stand
- Graph paper

1 Finding the speed of the car at different points along the ramp

Using two photogates far apart gives you a measure of the average speed of the car between the photogates. The car could be going faster at the lower photogate and slower at the upper one. To get a true picture of how the speed of the car changes, you will need to measure the speed with one photogate.

The car going through one photogate

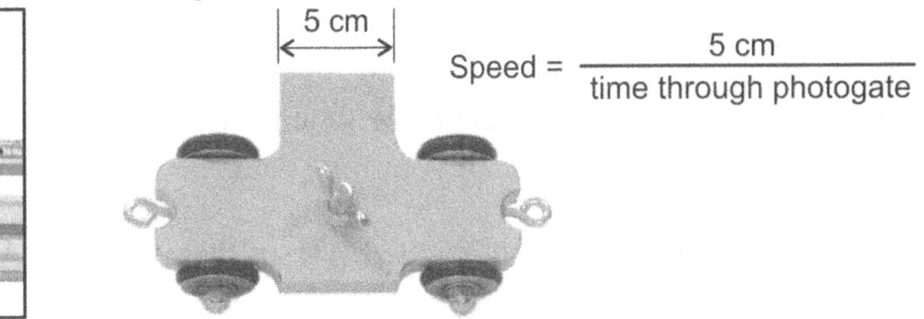

Remember, with one photogate the timer measures the time that the beam is broken. As the car passes through the photogate, the light beam is broken for the width of the wing. The speed of the car is the width of the wing (distance traveled) divided by the time it takes to pass through the light beam (time taken). The advantage to this technique is that it is easy to move a single photogate up and down the ramp to make measurements of the speed at many places.

2 Position versus time

1. Set up the ramp and physics stand at an angle given by your teacher.
2. Put photogate A at the 10 cm position.
3. Move photogate B to different positions 10 cm apart along the ramp.
4. For every position of photogate B, record the time through the beam at photogates A and B and also the time from A to B.
5. Take at least 8 data points along the ramp. Start the car the same way every time.

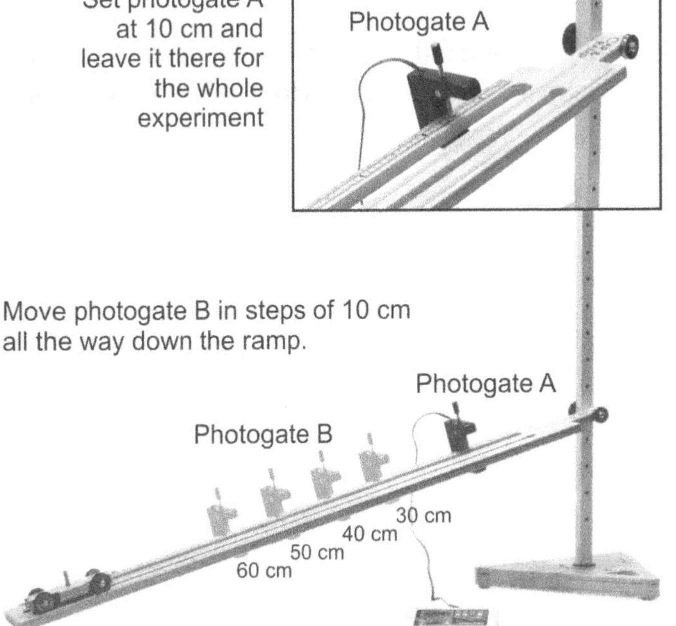

Table 1: Position versus time data

Position of photogate B (cm)	Time through photogate A (s)	Time through photogate B (s)	Time from photogate A to B (s)

3 Making the position versus time graph

a. The y-axis of your graph is going to be the position of photogate B. Choose a scale for the y-axis that goes from zero to your largest position.

b. The *x*-axis of your graph is the time from A to B. Pick a scale for the *x*-axis that fits all your time data.

c. Plot the position of photogate B versus the time from A to B.

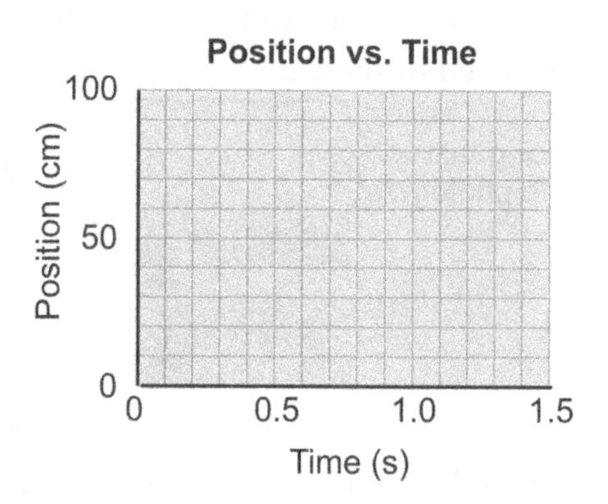

4 Stop and think

a. What shape does the position versus time graph have? Use words such as "curved," "straight," "increasing," or "decreasing" to describe the shape of your graph.

b. Calculate the average speed of the car from the graph or your data.

c. How long would it take the car to travel a distance of 2 meters at its average speed?

d. You recorded the time from photogate A each time you moved photogate B. What do you notice about the photogate A times? How is this information useful?

5 Find the car's speed from data in Table 1

Another way to describe the car's motion is to show how its speed changes with each new time interval from A to B. You will create a second data table, using some data from Table 1, and also entering some of your own calculations.

1. Copy the following data from Table 1 into Table 2: position of photogate B, time from A to B, and time through photogate B.
2. How far did the car travel as it went through photogate B each time? It is equal to the width of the car's wing. Record this distance in the third column of Table 2.
3. How fast is the car going at each photogate position? Calculate the speed of the car at each different position of photogate B. Use the distance and time you have already listed in Table 2 for your speed calculations. If you are confused about this calculation, re-read Part 1 of this investigation for an explanation of how it works.

Table 2: Speed of the car at photogate B

Position of photogate B (cm)	Time from photogate A to B (s)	Distance car traveled as it went through photogate B (cm)	Time through photogate B (s)	Speed of car at photogate B (cm/s)

6 The speed versus time graph

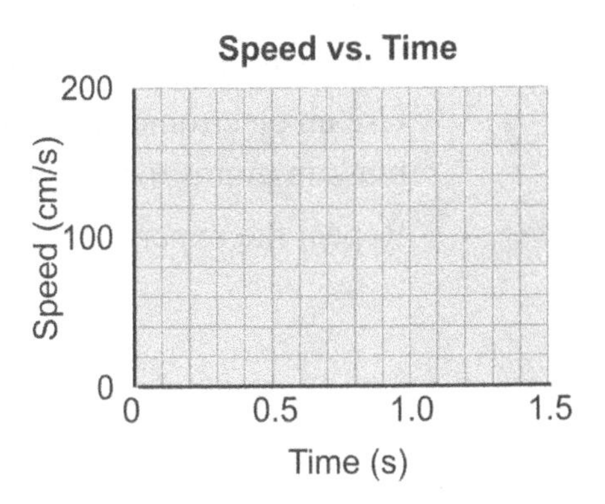

a. The *y*-axis of this graph is going to be the speed of the car at photogate B. Choose a scale for the *y*-axis that goes from zero to your largest speed.

b. The x-axis of your graph is the time from A to B.

c. Plot the speed at B versus the time from A to B.

d. What shape does the speed versus time graph have? Use words such as "curved," "straight," "increasing," or "decreasing" to describe the shape of your graph.

e. How does the speed of the car over the whole ramp compare to its average speed?

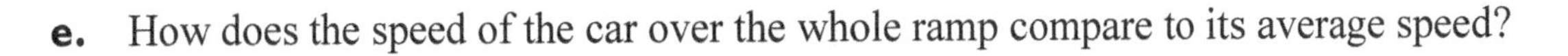

4A What is a Newton?

What is force and how is it measured?

You can think of force as a push or pull. Objects interact with each other (and you) through forces. It takes force to start an object's motion, and also force to stop an object in motion. This investigation will explore the precise definition of force and measure the strength of forces.

Materials

- Spring scale (0 - 5 N)
- 15 round metal washers (1/2 inch inner diam.)
- Loop of string
- Electronic scale (or triple beam balance)

1 Measuring forces

Forces have two important properties: strength and direction. In the English system of units, the strength of a force is measured in pounds. When you measure your own weight in pounds, you are measuring the force of gravity acting on your body. In the metric system, the strength of a force is measured in newtons (N). A quarter-pound hamburger has a weight of about 1 newton (1 lb = 4.448 N).

1. In the laboratory, you can measure force with a spring scale. Before using the spring scale however, you must be sure it correctly starts at zero. Calibrate the spring scale by turning the nut on the top until the plunger lines up with the zero mark.
2. Pull on the hook so the spring extends. When you pull, you are applying a force. Can you make a force of two newtons (2 N)?

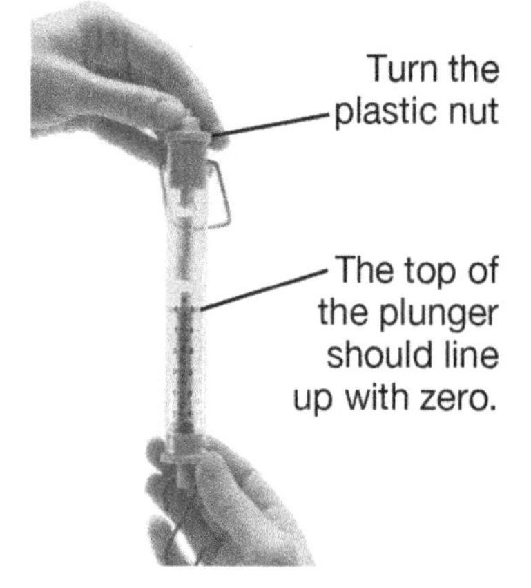

2 Weight: the force of gravity

Weight is one of the most common forces. Objects that have mass also have weight. Weight comes from the action of gravity on an object's mass.

1. Attach 3 steel washers to a loop of string.
2. Use a calibrated spring scale to measure the weight of the washers in newtons (N).
3. Use an electronic scale or triple beam balance to measure the mass in grams (g). Convert each mass in grams to kilograms (divide by 1000 or move decimal point three places to the left).
4. Repeat the experiment for 6, 9, 12, and 15 washers.

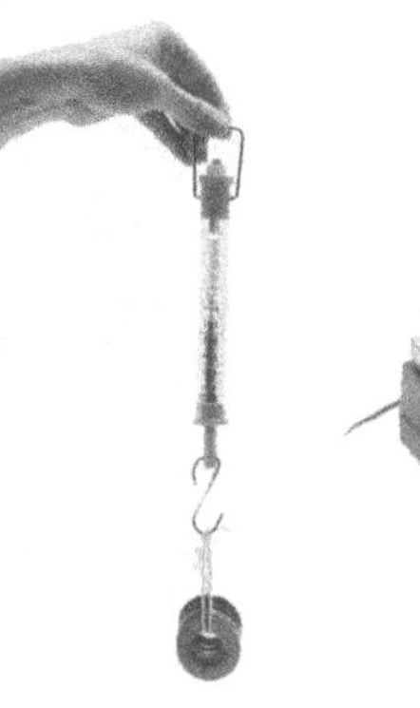

Find the weight in Newtons

Find the mass in grams, then convert to kilograms

Table 1: Weight and Mass Data

Number of washers	Weight (N)	Mass (kg)
3		
6		
9		
12		
15		

3 Stop and think

What do the results of your experiment tell you about the relationship between weight in newtons and mass in kilograms? Create a graph as described below to answer this question.

a. Make a graph of your data from Table 1. Place weight on the y-axis and mass on the x-axis.

b. Describe the graph. What does it tell you about the relationship between mass and weight?

c. At Earth's surface, the strength of gravity is about 9.8 newtons per kilogram. What does this number mean?

d. If an object has a mass of 10 kilograms, how much does it weigh in newtons?

4 Applying what you have learned

a. Explain how you could estimate the weight and mass of seven of your steel washers.

b. Find the weight and mass for seven of your steel washers. How close is the actual value to your estimated value? Give reasons for differences.

4B Friction

How does friction affect motion?

Friction is always present. It is a force that comes from motion — even through air! Sometimes friction is helpful — it's much easier to walk on a rough sidewalk than on a smooth patch of ice. Other times, we want friction to be small — oiling a bicycle chain reduces friction. This investigation will examine how air friction affects the car's motion on the ramp.

Materials

- Car and Ramp
- Physics Stand
- CPO Timer and photogates
- Tongue depressor
- Large paper plate
- Tape

1 Control setup

The first thing to do is see how the car performs before we add extra friction.

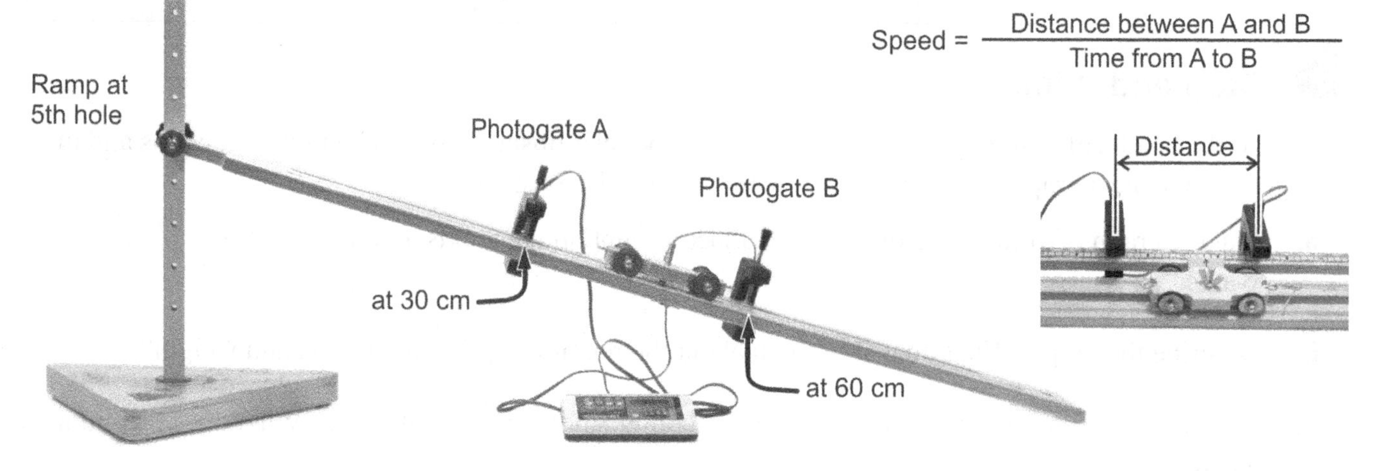

1. Attach the ramp to the physics stand at the fifth hole from the bottom.
2. Place photogate A at 30 cm, and photogate B at 60 cm.
3. Let the car roll down the ramp, and record the time from A to B.
4. Calculate the average speed of the car.
5. Repeat two more times, for a total of three trials.
6. Calculate the average speed from your three trials.

Table 1: Control Speeds

Trial	Distance A to B (cm)	Time A to B (s)	Speed (cm/s)
1			
2			
3			
		Average Speed	

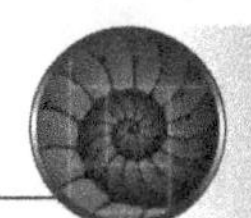

2 Create the "sail" car

A paper plate "sail" adds air friction (drag) to the car.

1. Tape a tongue depressor to the paper plate. Attach this assembly to the car as shown. Use enough tape to firmly attach the tongue depressor (after removing the wing nut) to the threaded spindle on top of the car.

Experimental car

3 Your hypothesis

a. Write a hypothesis that compares the speeds of the "sail car" and the normal car.

b. Explain the reasoning behind your hypothesis.

4 Do the experiment

1. The ramp and photogates should be set up as in Part 1.
2. Let the experimental car roll down the ramp, and record the time from A to B.
3. Calculate the average speed of the car.
4. Repeat two more times, for a total of three trials.
5. Calculate the average speed from your three trials.

Experimental setup

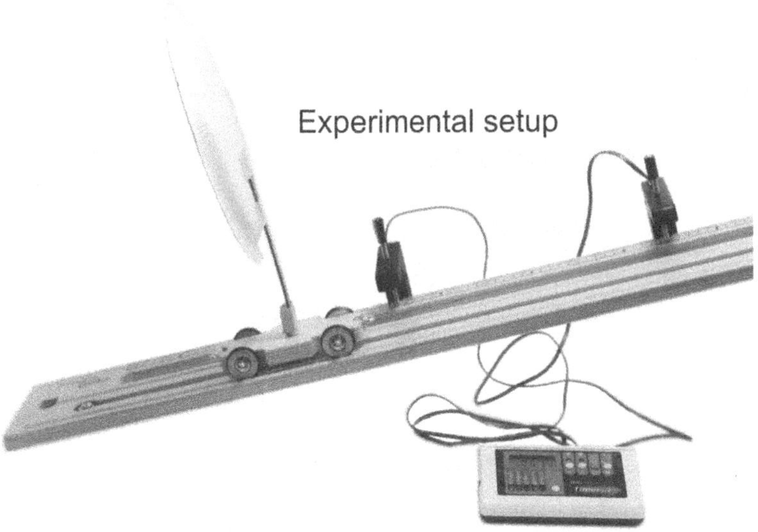

Table 2: Experimental Speeds

Trial	Distance A to B (cm)	Time A to B (s)	Speed (cm/s)
1			
2			
3			
		Average Speed	

5 Stop and think

a. Did your results confirm your hypothesis? Explain.

b. How did air friction affect the car's motion?

6 Applying what you have learned

a. Friction is a force that opposes motion. Explain where the friction force on the sail comes from.

b. Is the sail the only source of friction? Does the car have any friction forces acting on it other than air friction? Explain.

5A Force and Acceleration

What happens when force is applied to something that can move?

Forces affect motion, but exactly how is motion affected? Do objects continue to move? Do they speed up or slow down? In this investigation you will see that force causes acceleration. The effect of force is to change speed, resulting in acceleration.

Materials

- CPO Timer and 1 photogate
- Car and Ramp
- Physics Stand
- 50 g of clay
- 1.25 meters of string with a clip
- Lanyard clip
- Level
- Meter stick
- Indelible fine point marker or pen
- Masking tape

1 Pulling the car with a force

1. Stick a small piece of tape on the wing of the car and draw an arrow in the center.
2. Set the end of the ramp on a table or chair. Attach the ramp to the physics stand so the ramp is flat.
3. Use a level to get the ramp as level as you can. You may need to shim up the end of the ramp to get it level.
4. Attach the string to the end of the car with the clip. Attach a clay ball about 4 cm in diameter to the string. Position the clay ball so it is just below the pulley when the car is at the end of the ramp.
5. Pull the car to the end of the ramp and let it go. It should roll up the ramp as the clay falls and keep rolling until it hits the other end of the ramp.

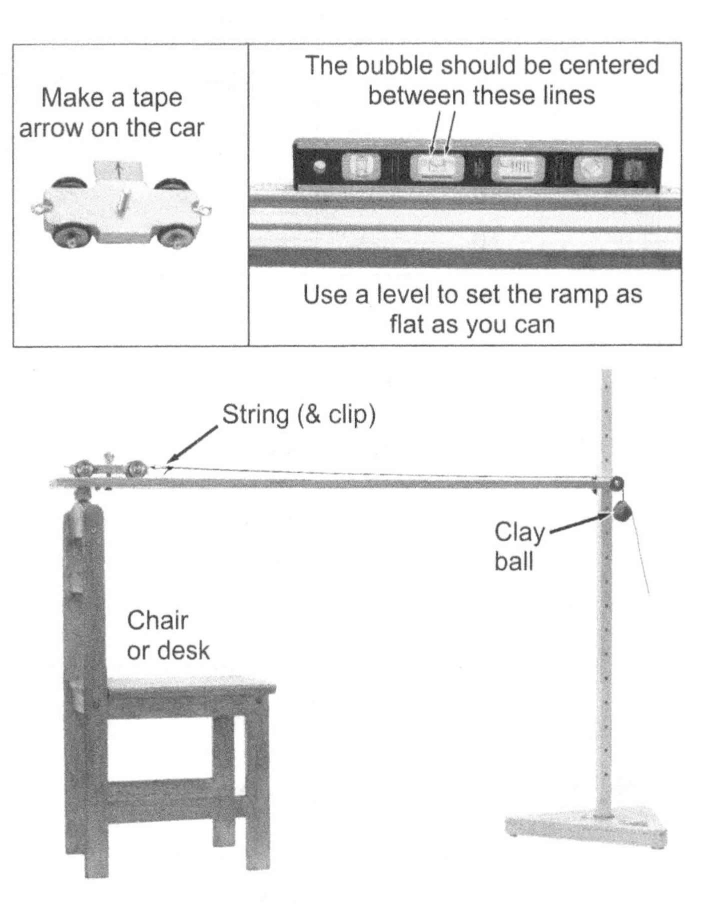

2 Stop and think

a. What is the purpose of the clay ball and string?

b. What is the car's position when the clay ball hits the ground?

c. Where on the ramp is the string exerting a force on the car?

d. Where on the ramp is the force from the string zero?

3 Measuring acceleration

We want to know how the speed of the car is affected by the force from the string. The car moves the length of the wing (5 cm) during the time the light beam is broken. The speed of the car is 5 cm ÷ time, where "time" is the time it takes to pass through ONE photogate.

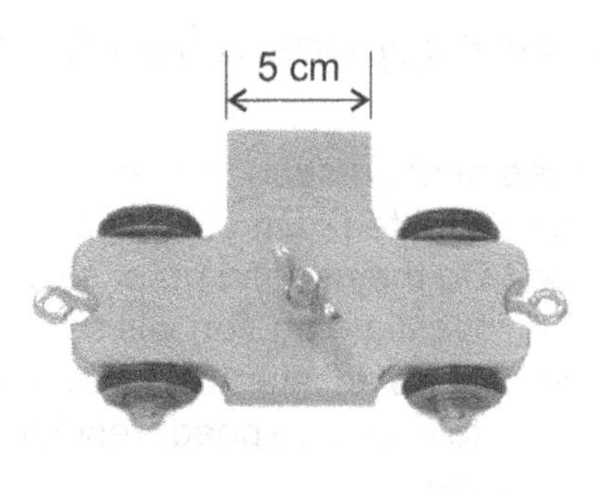

1. Put photogate A at 80 cm.
2. Let the car roll and record the time it takes the car to pass through the photogate.
3. Move the photogate to 60 cm, 50 cm... and every 10 cm along the ramp. Record the time through the photogate for each new position.
4. Calculate the speed of the car at each position by dividing 5 cm by the photogate time.

$$\text{Speed} = \frac{5\text{ cm}}{\text{time through photogate}}$$

Table 1: Position, speed, and time data

Position of photogate (cm)	Time through photogate (s)	Speed at photogate (cm/s)
80		
70		
60		

4 Looking at the data

a. How does the speed of the car change along the ramp?

b. Make a graph that shows the speed of the car every 10 cm along the ramp. It is easiest to understand this graph if the position counts down from left to right, like the diagram.

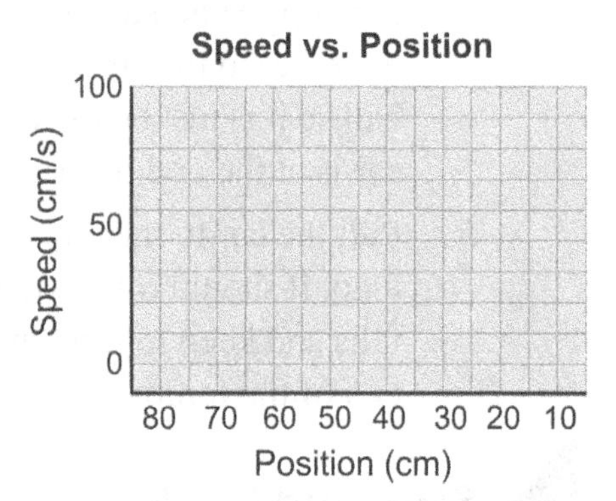

c. You should see the graph change at one point on the ramp. What change do you see and why do you think this change occurred?

5 Thinking about the motion

a. Label the part of your graph that shows where the string was pulling on the car. How does this part of the graph differ from the rest of the graph?

b. Write a sentence that connects the idea of force to the idea of acceleration.

c. How does your experiment support the sentence you just wrote?

d. What happens to the speed of the car after the clay ball hits the floor? Why?

e. Describe the net force on the car before and after the clay hits the floor.

5B Newton's Second Law

How does acceleration depend on force and mass?

In the last investigation you saw that a net force causes acceleration. In this investigation we will look at how the acceleration depends on the strength of the force and the mass of the car.

Materials

- CPO Timer and 1 photogate
- Car and Ramp
- Physics Stand
- Balance or digital scale
- 80 g of clay
- 3 steel weights
- 1.25 meters of string
- Lanyard clip
- Level
- Meter stick
- Small piece of masking tape

1 Acceleration and mass

In this part of the investigation, the force is going to stay the same. Mass is going to change.

1. Set the car and ramp up like you did in Investigation 5A. Make sure the ramp is level. Measure out 40 grams of clay from the 80 grams you were given.
2. Tape and mark the car's starting point on the ramp.
3. Move the photogate until the timer reads close to 0.1000 seconds when the car rolls through. This is where the speed of the car is 50 cm/s.
4. Measure and record the distance from the start to the photogate.
5. Add 1 weight to the car and move the photogate until the time is about 0.1000 seconds again.
6. Measure the new distance then repeat the experiment for 2 weights.

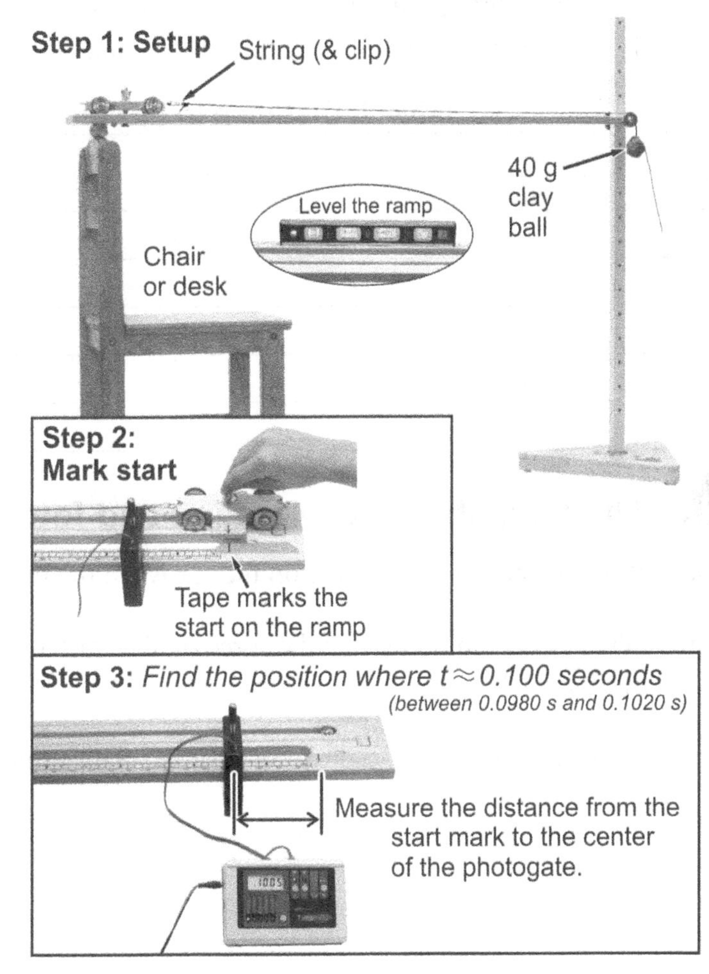

Table 1: Distance to 50 cm/s with 40 g of clay

Time through photogate (s)	Distance from start to photogate (cm)	Weights
		0
		1
		2

2 Thinking about acceleration and mass

The force of the string makes the car accelerate. As a result the car's speed changes over a distance.

a. Suppose it takes the car 30 cm to reach 50 cm/s. If the acceleration is GREATER will this distance increase, decrease, or stay about the same?

b. Do your results show a direct or inverse relationship between mass and acceleration?

3 Acceleration and force

Now the mass of the car will stay the same and the force pulling the car will change.

1. Copy the data from the last row of Table 1 into the first row of Table 2.
2. Measure 10 grams of clay from the piece of clay you set aside in part 1. Add the 10 grams to the clay hanging on the string, making the total mass 50 grams.
3. Release the car and measure the time. Move the photogate until the timer reads close to 0.1000 seconds, as you did in part 1. Record the time through the photogate and the distance between the car's starting position and the photogate.
4. Repeat the experiment with a 60, 70, and 80-gram clay ball.

Table 2: Distance to 50 cm/s with various masses of clay

Time through photogate (s)	Distance from start to photogate (cm)	Mass of clay ball (g)
		40
		50
		60
		70
		80

4 Thinking about acceleration and force

a. What happened to the force on the car when the mass of the clay increased?

b. What effect did increasing the force on the car have on the distance it took for the car to reach a speed of 50 cm/s?

c. Do your results show a direct or inverse relationship between force and acceleration?

5 Possible forms of the second law

There are lots of ways we could write a relationship between force, mass, and acceleration. Most of them would be wrong because they wouldn't agree with the experiment. Only one of the following relationships is correct. The other three CAN'T be correct because if they WERE, they would disagree with our experiment. Explain why (b) and (c) can't be correct. Explain why (d) could be correct. An example explanation is given for why (a) cannot be correct.

a. Acceleration = Force + Mass *(solution: If this were true, then increasing the mass should have made the acceleration increase (shorter distance). Our experiment showed that increasing the mass made the acceleration decrease (longer distance). Therefore, the relationship "acceleration = force + mass" cannot logically be correct.*

b. Acceleration = Force - Mass

c. Acceleration = Force × Mass

d. Acceleration = Force ÷ Mass

6A Energy Transformations on a Roller Coaster

Where does the marble move the fastest, and why?

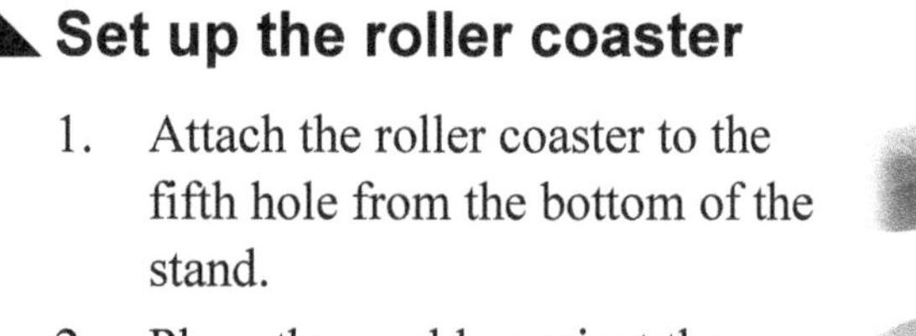

To pedal your bicycle up a hill, you have to work hard to keep the bicycle moving. However, when you start down the other side of the hill, you can coast. In this investigation, you will see how a marble's speed changes as it moves up and down hills. It's all about energy.

Materials

- CPO Roller Coaster
- Steel marble
- CPO Timer and photogates
- Meter stick
- Physics Stand

1 Set up the roller coaster

1. Attach the roller coaster to the fifth hole from the bottom of the stand.
2. Place the marble against the starting peg and let it roll down the track.
3. Watch the marble roll along the track. Where do you think it moves the fastest?

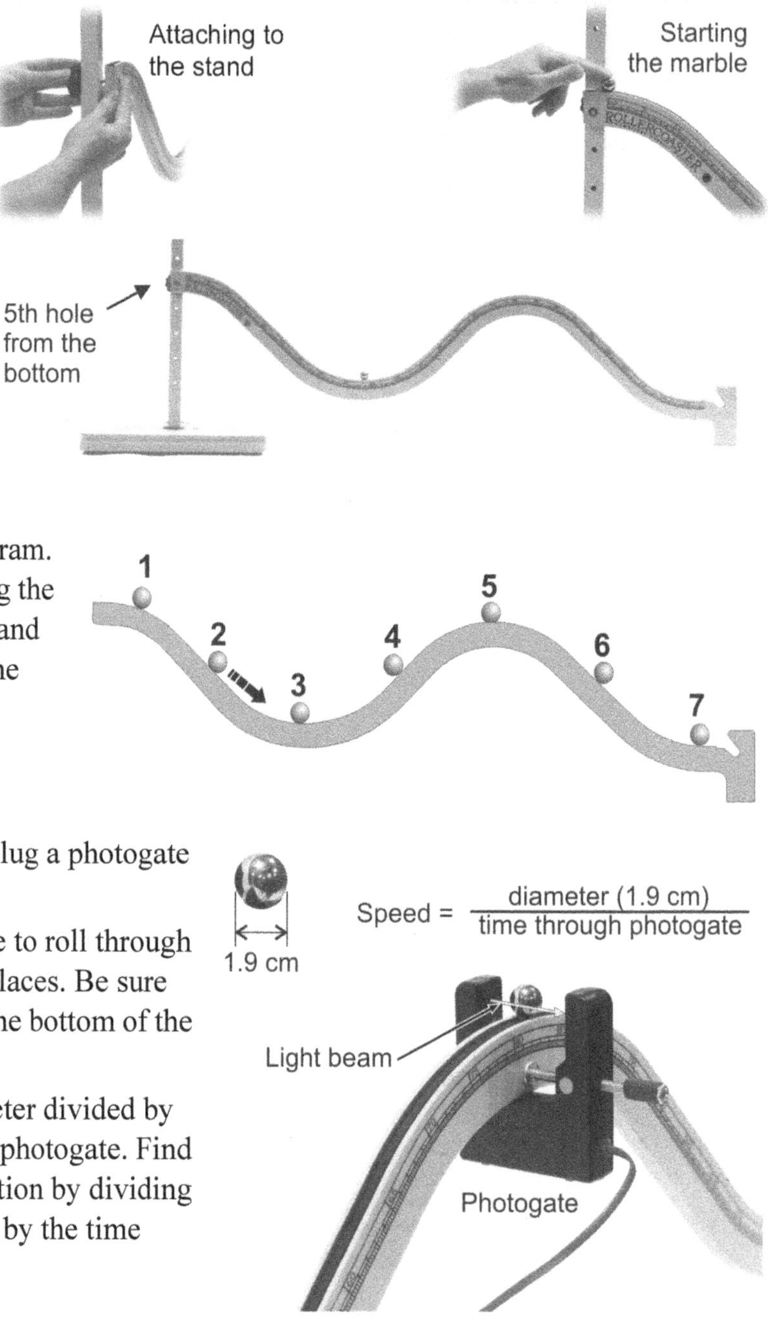

2 A hypothesis

a. Think about the seven places in the diagram. Where do you think the marble is moving the fastest? Choose one of the seven places and write down why you think that will be the fastest place.

3 Testing your idea

1. Set the timer in interval mode and plug a photogate into input "A."
2. Measure the time it takes the marble to roll through the photogate at each of the seven places. Be sure the photogate is pushed up against the bottom of the track.
3. The speed of the marble is its diameter divided by the time it takes to pass through the photogate. Find the speed of the marble at each position by dividing the diameter of the marble (1.9 cm) by the time through photogate A.

$$\text{Speed} = \frac{\text{diameter (1.9 cm)}}{\text{time through photogate}}$$

Table 1: Speed of the Marble

Position	Distance (cm)	Time A (s)	Speed (cm/s)
1	1.9		
2	1.9		
3	1.9		
4	1.9		
5	1.9		
6	1.9		
7	1.9		

4 Stop and think

a. Which position was fastest?

b. Propose an explanation for why that place was fastest.

c. The marble has more potential energy at the top of the roller coaster than at the bottom. What happens to this energy?

d. It takes energy to increase the marble's speed. Where does this energy come from?

5 Energy and change

1. Measure the speed and height of the marble every 10 cm along the roller coaster.

Table 2: Speed and height data

Position (cm)	Height (cm)	Time A (s)	Speed (cm/s)
10			
20			
30			
40			
50			
60			

a. Make a graph with the height on the y-axis and the position on the x-axis.

b. Scale the right hand side so you can plot speed on the same graph. Use the example in the diagram.

c. What does the graph tell you about the relationship between speed and height?

d. Explain the graph in terms of potential energy, kinetic energy, and total energy.

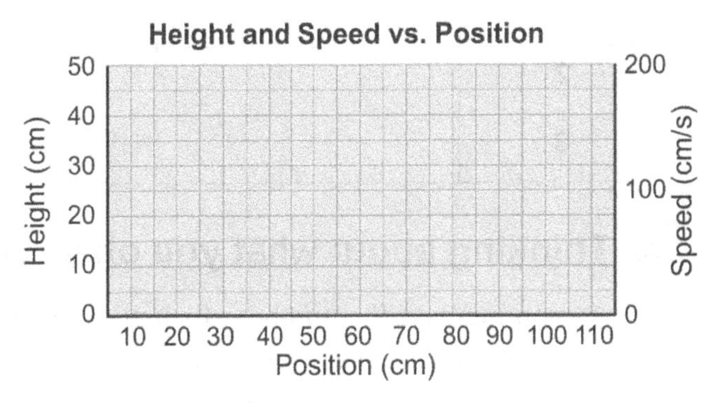

6B Force, Work and Machines

How do simple machines operate?

Machines are things humans invent to make tasks easier. Simple machines use directly applied forces. Simple machines allowed humans to build the great pyramids and other monuments using only muscle power. This Investigation is about how simple machines use force to accomplish a task.

Materials

- Ropes and Pulleys
- Spring scales
- Physics Stand
- Four steel weights
- Meter stick

1 Building a simple machine

1. Attach four weights to the bottom block. Use a spring scale to measure the weight of the bottom block and record it as the output force.
2. Attach the top block near the top of the physics stand.
3. Thread the yellow string over one or more of the pulleys of the top and bottom pulley blocks. The yellow string can be clipped to either the top block or the bottom block.
4. Build combinations with 1, 2, 3, 4, 5, and 6 supporting strings directly supporting the bottom block. (Hint: 1, 3, and 5 have the string clipped to the bottom block. 2, 4, and 6 have the string clipped to the top block)
5. Use a force scale to measure the force needed to slowly lift the bottom block for different combinations of supporting strings.

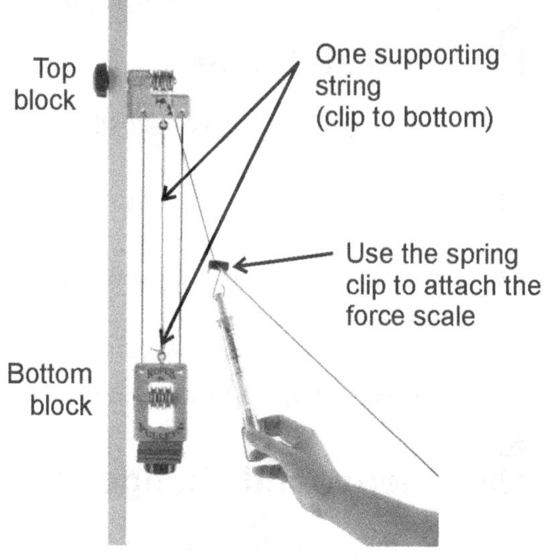

Measuring the input force

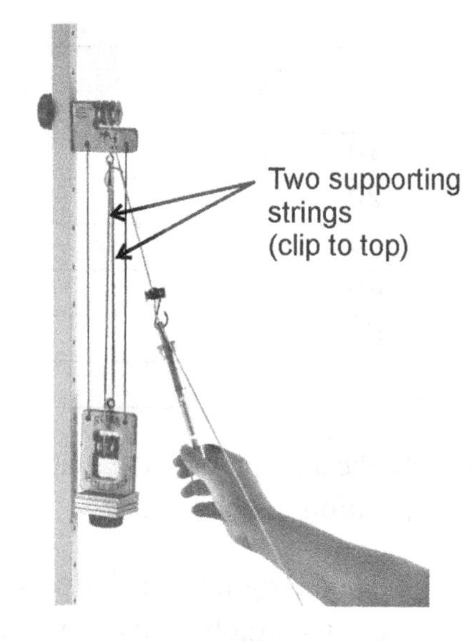

Safety Tip: Don't pull sideways, or you can tip the stand over!

Table 1: Input and Output Forces

Number of supporting strings	Input force (newtons)	Output force (newtons)
1		
2		
3		

2 Thinking about what you observed

a. As you increase the number of supporting strings, what happens to the force needed to lift the bottom block?

b. Write a rule that relates the number of pulleys, input force, and output force.

c. Research the term "mechanical advantage." What does this mean for a simple machine?

d. Use your data from Table 1 to calculate the mechanical advantage for each arrangement of supporting strings.

3 The input and output distance

1. Use the marker stop (cord stop) to mark where the string leaves the top pulley.
2. Choose a distance that you will lift the bottom pulley during each trial of the experiment. This is the **output distance**. Your output distance should be at least 20 centimeters.
3. Pull the yellow string to lift the block your chosen distance.
4. Measure how much string length you had to pull to lift the block. This is the **input distance**.
5. Measure the input and output distances for each of the different configurations (1, 2, 3, 4, 5, and 6)
6. Copy your Input force and Output force data from part 1 into Table 2.

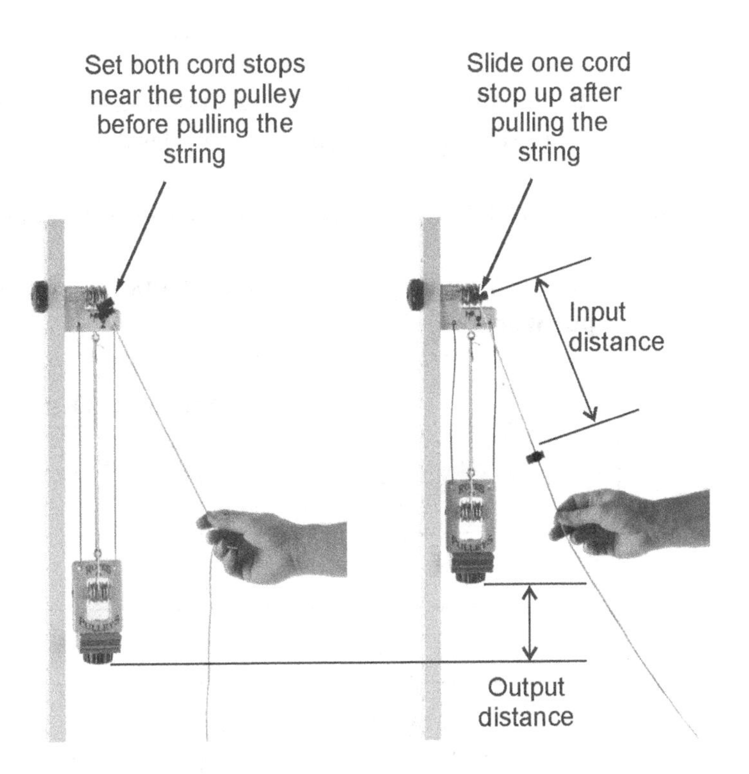

Measuring the input and output distance

Table 2: Force and Distance Data

Mechanical advantage	Output force (newtons)	Output distance (meters)	Input force (newtons)	Input distance (meters)
1				
2				
3				
4				

4 Thinking about what you observed

a. As the mechanical advantage increases, what happens to the length of the string you have to pull to raise the block?

b. The word *work* is used in many different ways. For example, you *work* on science problems, your toaster doesn't *work*, or taking out the trash is too much *work*. In science, however, *work* has one specific meaning. Write one sentence that defines work in its scientific meaning.

c. You may have heard the saying, "nothing is free." Explain why this is true of the ropes and pulleys. (HINT: What do you trade for using less input force to lift the block?)

d. Use your data to calculate the work done on the block (the **output work**).

e. Next, use your data to calculate the work you did as you pulled on the string to lift the block. This is the **input work**.

Table 3: Output and Input Work

Mechanical advantage	Output work (joules)	Input work (joules)
1		
2		
3		
4		
5		
6		

The rules of simple machines

a. For each mechanical advantage, how do output and input work compare?

b. Is output work ever greater than input work? Can you explain this?

c. Explain any differences between input and output work in your data.

7A Phases of the Moon

Why does it look like the moon's shape changes?

The moon reflects sunlight, and when one entire sunlit side of the moon faces Earth, we can see a bright full moon. Why does the moon seem to change its shape throughout the month? The moon is always round, and the sun always shines on half the moon, but we see the moon from different angles. In this investigation, you will set up a model to view the "moon" from different angles.

Materials

- Flashlight (a bright one; LED is best)
- 6-inch plastic foam sphere (spray-painted gray)
- 12-inch green paper circle
- Pencil
- Masking tape

The moon's phases (new moon, crescent moon, quarter moon, full moon) change regularly each month. To simulate these phases and study them, you will set up a model of the Earth, moon, and sun system.

1 Modeling moon phases

1. Carefully poke the pencil's sharpened end into the plastic foam ball to make a handle.
2. Tape the green paper circle to the floor. This represents Earth.
3. Assign group roles for the start of the experiment. You will switch roles and repeat so everyone gets a turn. The roles are: Manager, Moon, Earth Observer, and Sun.
4. Once you understand your role in making the model work, perform the experiment multiple times so everyone in the group has a turn being the Earth Observer.
5. NEVER look directly into the flashlight!

2 Thinking about what you observed

a. Describe how the lit portion of the moon changed as the moon revolved. Use sketches to illustrate your description.

b. The moon's shape doesn't change throughout the month — it is always a sphere. But why does it APPEAR as though the moon's shape changes? What is actually changing?

c. How much time goes by from one new moon to the next?

3 Moon Phase Challenge

1. Study the moon phases and their names in the diagram below.
2. Assign each group member a role in the Earth/moon/sun model.
3. Your teacher will call out the name of a moon phase. Assemble your model so the correct moon phase is demonstrated for the Earth Observer. Your teacher will check your setup.
4. Choose a moon phase to model. See if another group can figure out which moon phase you are modeling for the Earth Observer.

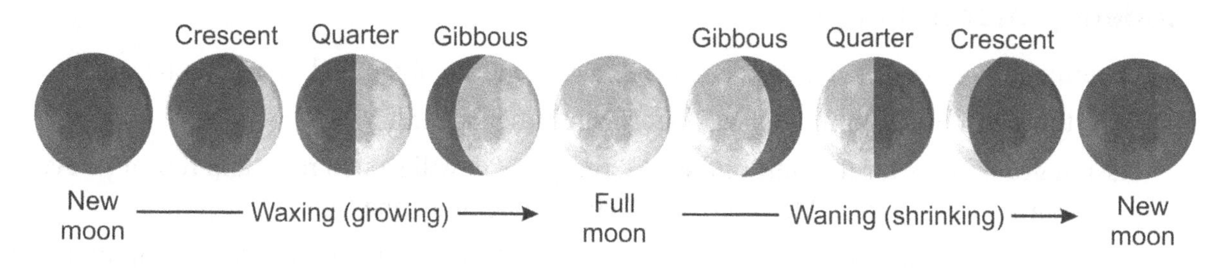

4 Explore on your own

a. Make a moon phase flip book! Use a small note pad; the kind that has the low-tack adhesive at the top that allows it to be stuck and unstuck from other paper works well. You will need about 25 sheets on the note pad. Starting with a new moon, draw the phases of the moon, slowly advancing from new moon to full moon and back again, changing each moon slightly on each new page. When you flip through the note pad, you will see a "movie" of the moon as it changes from one phase to another during a one month period. There are many examples of moon phase flip books on the Internet. See how your flip book compares to others!

b. The same side of the moon always faces Earth. Explain why this is, and create a simple demonstration that shows how this happens.

c. What is a lunar eclipse? Do a little research, and explain how you could model a lunar eclipse by adding to the Earth/moon/sun model you used in this investigation.

d. What is a solar eclipse? Do a little research, and explain how you could model a solar eclipse by adding to the Earth/moon/sun model you used in this investigation.

7B The Size of the Solar System

How big is the Solar System?

It is difficult to comprehend great distances. For example, how great a distance is 150,000,000 kilometers, the distance from Earth to the sun? One way to get a sense of these distances is to create a scale model. A globe is a scale model of Earth and road maps are scale models of geographic regions. Scale models help us visualize the true sizes of objects and the distances between them. In this Investigation, you will make a scale model representing distances in the Solar System. The results may surprise you.

Materials

- Metric track and field tape measure (25 m or more) or a trundle wheel

1 Setting up

1. Make signs for each of the planets and one for the sun.
2. Find an area that is at least 100-meters long. Choose a location at one end for the sun.

Neptune is 30 AU (5.9 billion kilometers) from the sun. We can use a *proportion* to determine a scale distance for our model. For this investigation, we will use 100 meters as the scale distance between the sun and Neptune. The diagram below shows the planets with Neptune at its correct distance of 30 AU. The diagram also shows a 100 meter scale. You can use the diagram to determine the proportional distances from the sun to the other planets.

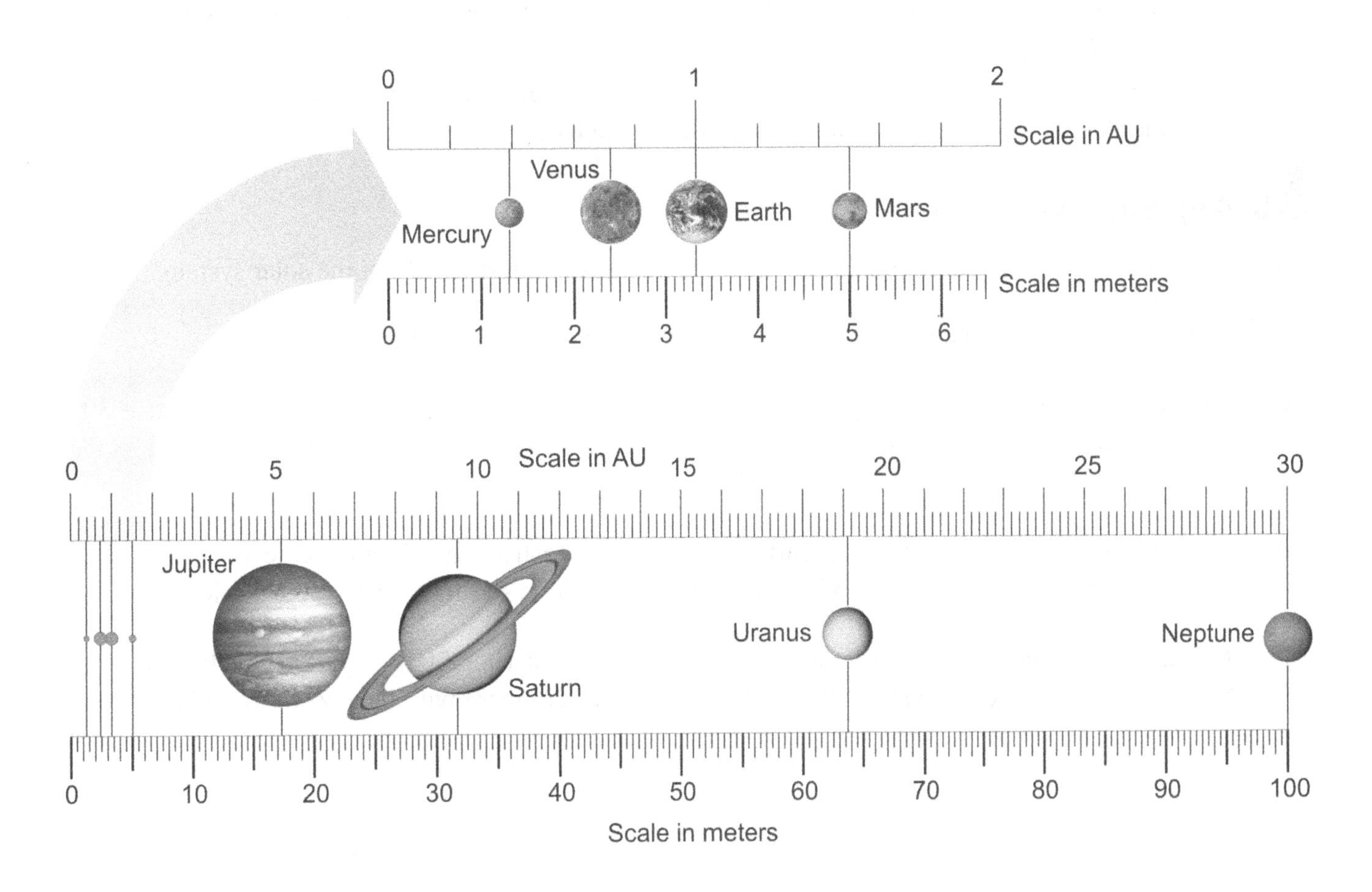

2 Determining scale distances for the other planets

1. According to the diagram, Mercury is 1.3 meters from the sun at the 100 meter scale.
2. Determine the scaled distances from the sun to the other planets. Write the distance in meters for each planet in Table 1.

Table 1: Scale distances from the sun to the planets

Planet	Diameter (km)	Actual distance to sun (km)	(AU)	Scale distance from the sun (m)
Mercury	4,878	58,000,000	0.39	1.3
Venus	12,100	108,000,000	0.72	
Earth	12,760	150,000,000	1.0	
Mars	6,786	228,000,000	1.5	
Jupiter	142,800	778,000,000	5.2	
Saturn	120,000	1,430,000,000	9.5	
Uranus	50,800	2,870,000,000	19.1	
Neptune	48,600	4,500,000,000	30.0	

Making the model

1. A student should stand in the zero-meter position with a sign that says "Sun."
2. Measure 100 meters from the position of the sun. At the 100-meter mark, a student will stand with a sign that says "Neptune."
3. Now, use the scale distances from Table 1 to find the locations of each planet. A student should hold the appropriate sign at the position of each planet.

4 Applying what you have learned

a. After "acting" the model, write down three impressions you formed about the solar system.

b. Describe some disadvantages and advantages to using this model of the solar system.

c. The planets in the diagram are shown FAR larger than they would be at a scale of 100 meters = 30 AU. At this scale, 1 millimeter = 45,000 kilometers of real distance. How big should the Earth be in the solar system model where 100 m = 30 AU?

d. Alpha Centauri is the closest star to Earth at 274,332 AU (astronomical units). One astronomical unit is equal to 150 million kilometers. Where would you place this star in the 100-meter scale model?

e. The diameter of the Milky Way galaxy is known to be about 100,000 light years. One light year is 63,000 AU. How does the size of the Milky Way galaxy compare with the size of the solar system?

8A Electricity

How does electricity work?

What happens when you turn on an electric light? Where does the light energy come from? The answer is electricity. We use electricity to store energy and to carry energy to where we need it.

Materials

- Electric circuits kit
- 1 "D" battery
- Pieces of foil, wood, plastic, metal paper clips, and other small objects.

1 Building a circuit

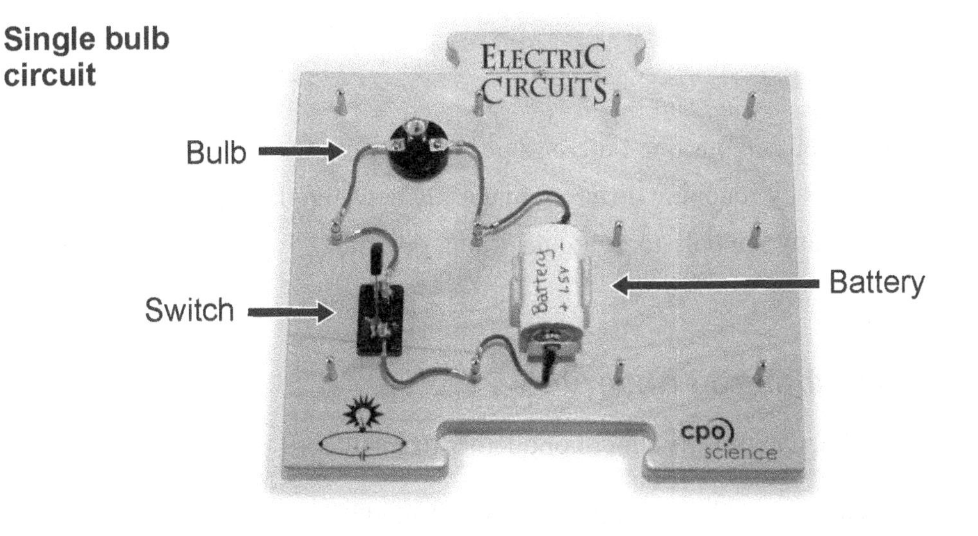

1. Build the circuit shown in the diagram with one battery, a switch, and a bulb.
2. Open and close the switch and see what happens.

2 Thinking about what you observed

a. How can you tell electric current is flowing in the circuit? Can you see the current?

b. Current flows from positive to negative. Trace the flow of current around the circuit with your finger.

c. How does the switch cause the current to stop flowing?

d. Why does the bulb go out when you open the switch?

3 Conductors and insulators

Materials in which electric current flows easily are called *conductors*.
Materials through which current does not flow through easily are called *insulators*.

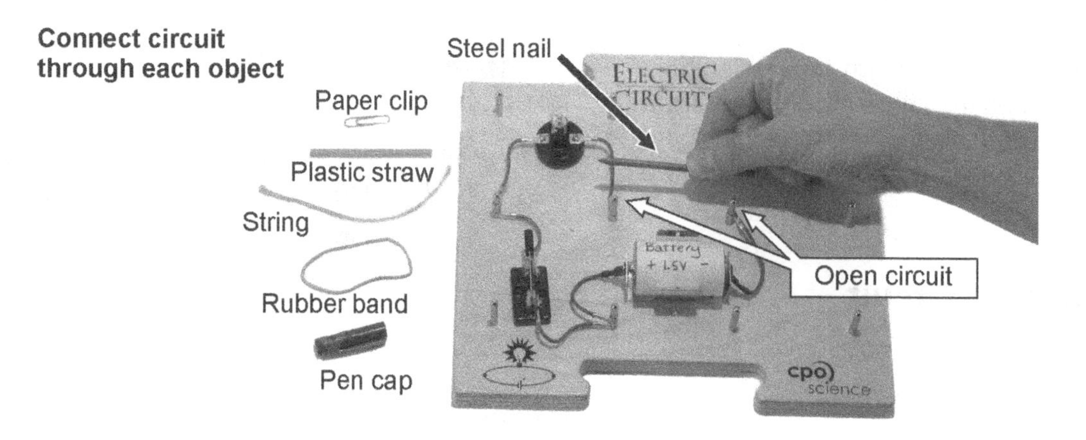

1. Break one connection in your one-bulb circuit.
2. Complete the circuit by touching different materials between the wire and the post.
3. Which materials allow the bulb to light and which do not?

4 Thinking about what you observed

a. Make a table listing the materials as either conductors or insulators.

b. What characteristics are shared by the conductors you found?

c. What characteristics are shared by the insulators you found?

5 Circuit diagrams

For describing electric circuits we use the language of *circuit diagrams*. In a circuit diagram wires are represented by solid lines. Electrical devices like switches, batteries, and bulbs are represented by symbols.

a. Using these symbols, draw a picture of the circuit you built with one battery, switch, and light bulb.

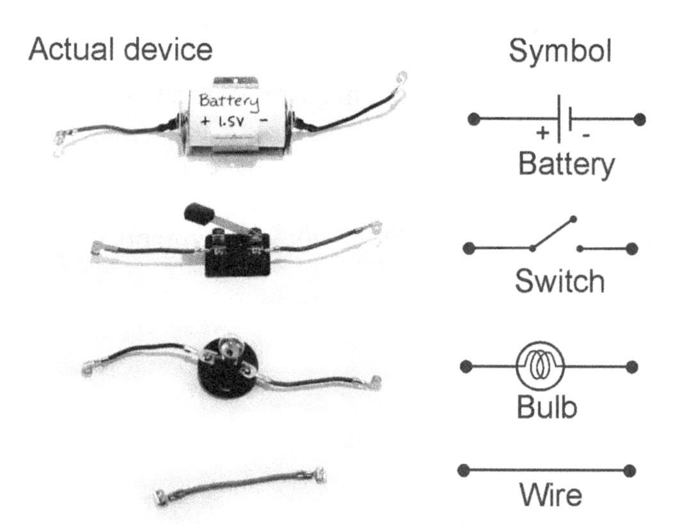

6 A series circuit

A *series circuit* has only one path for the electrical current. Build this series circuit and use your finger to trace the path taken by the current.

1. Build the circuit shown on the right with one battery, a switch, and two bulbs.
2. Open and close the switch and see what happens. Pay attention to the brightness of the bulbs.
3. Unscrew one of the bulbs part way. What happens?

7 Thinking about what you observed

a. Which of the three diagrams matches this circuit?

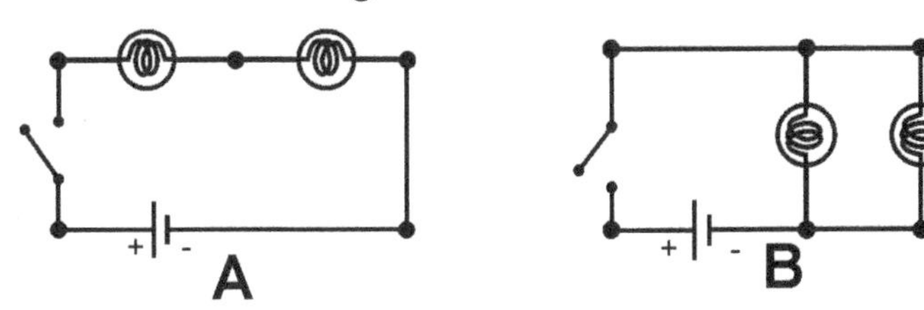

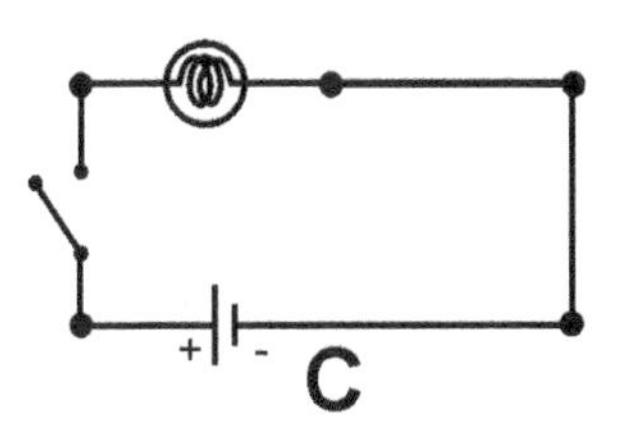

b. How does the brightness of the bulbs compare to the circuit with one bulb?

c. Can you explain the brightness difference using the idea of energy?

d. Can you explain why unscrewing one bulb made both bulbs go out?

8 A parallel circuit

A *parallel circuit* has more than one path for the electrical current. Build this parallel circuit and use your finger to trace each path taken by the current.

1. Build the circuit shown on the right with one battery, a switch, and two bulbs.
2. Open and close the switch and see what happens. Pay attention to the brightness of the bulbs.
3. Unscrew one of the bulbs part way. What happens?

9 Thinking about what you observed

a. Which of the three diagrams matches this circuit?

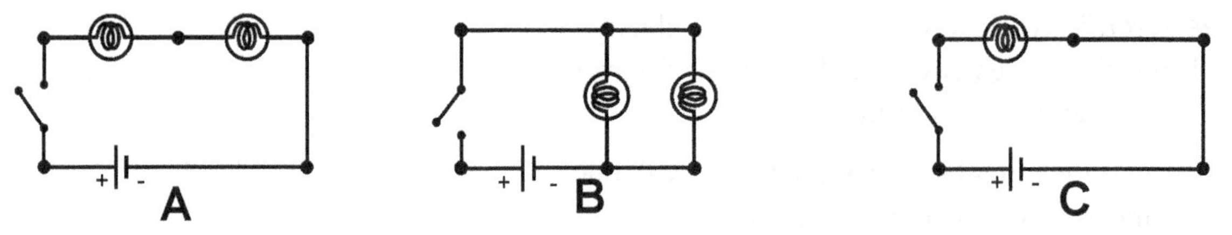

b. How does the brightness of the bulbs in this circuit compare to the series circuit bulbs?

c. Can you explain the brightness difference using the idea of energy?

d. Can you explain why unscrewing one bulb did NOT make the other bulb go out?

8B Magnetism

What are the properties of magnetism?

Magnets are used in almost all electrical and electronic machines from motors to computers and are able to exert strong forces at a distance. This Investigation will explore the properties of magnets.

Materials

- Electric circuits kit
- 1 "D" battery
- Magnets
- Metric ruler
- Coil

1 How far does magnetic force reach?

How far does the magnetic force of a magnet reach? This is an important question concerning machines such as motors and generators that use magnets.

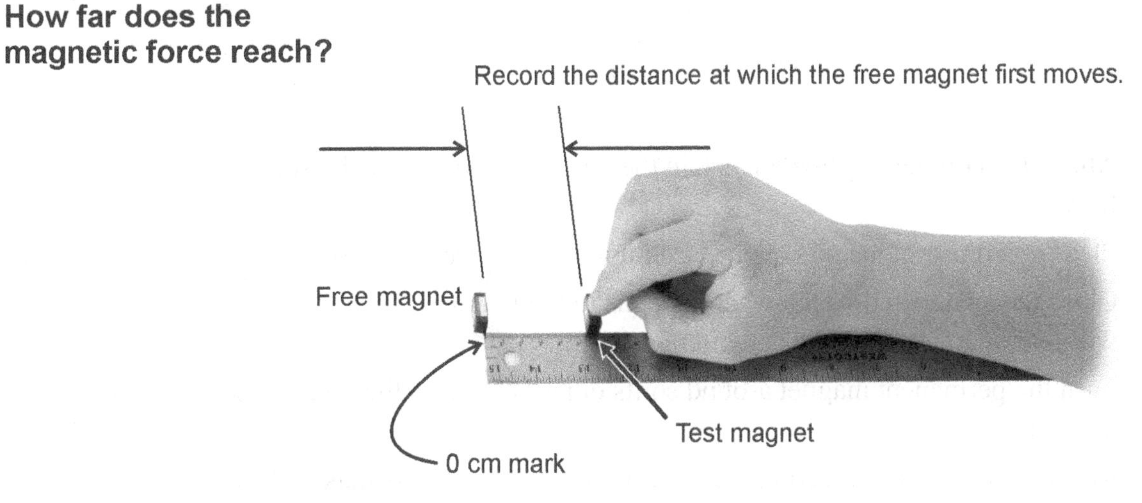

1. Place one magnet at the 0 cm mark of the ruler and slide a second magnet closer and closer until the first magnet moves. Practice the technique several times before recording data.
2. Record the distance between the magnets when you first see movement.
3. Try each of the combinations of poles—north-north, south-south, and north-south.
4. For each combination, complete three trials, and average your three distances.

Table 1: Force between two magnets

	North-South	South-South	North-North
Distance (mm)			

2 Thinking about what you observed

a. Look at your results and compare the distances for the three combinations of poles. Are the attract and repel distances *significantly* different? In science, "significantly" means the differences are large compared to the precision of your measurement.

3 Electromagnets

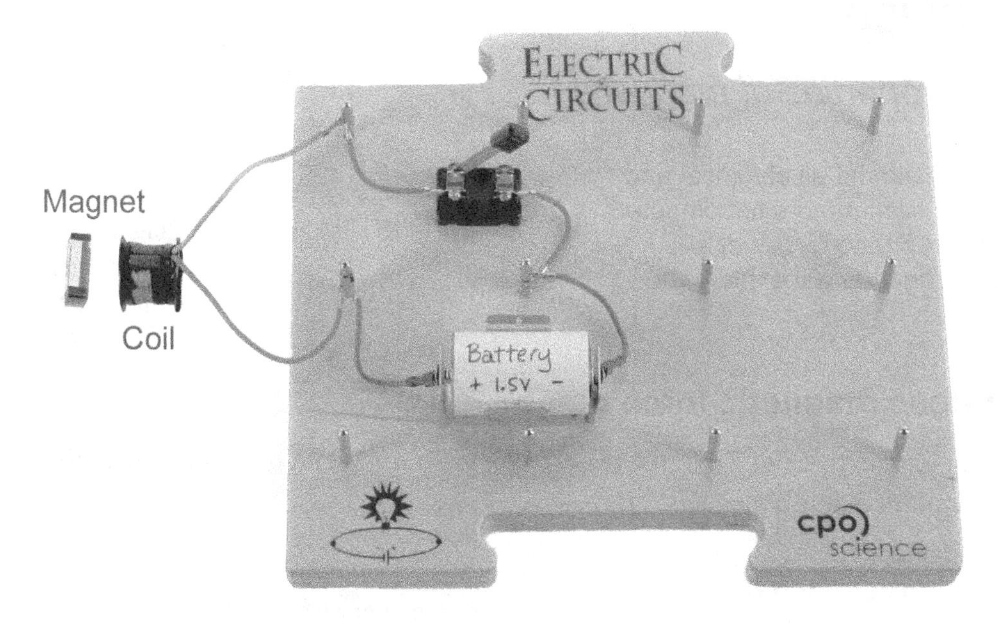

1. Attach the coil, battery, and switch in the circuit shown above. Leave the switch open so no current flows.
2. Place a permanent magnet about 1 centimeter away from the coil. Stand the magnet up on its end.
3. Close the switch and watch what happens to the magnet. DON'T leave current running or the coil will overheat. Open the switch after each trial.
4. Turn the permanent magnet around so its other pole faces the coil. Close the switch and see what happens now.
5. Reverse the wires connecting the battery to the circuit. This makes the electric current flow the other way. Repeat steps 3 and 4 of experiment with the magnet.

4 Thinking about what you observed

a. Write 2-3 sentences that explain what you saw when the switch was closed.

b. Propose an explanation for why the magnet moved.

c. When the magnet was reversed, did the force between it and the coil change direction? How did the force change?

d. When the coil wires were switched, did the force from the coil change direction? How do you know?

e. How is a coil of wire carrying current like a magnet? How is it different?

9A The Motion of a Pendulum

How do we describe back and forth, or repeating motion?

Harmonic motion is motion that repeats in cycles. Many things in nature and many human inventions involve harmonic motion. For example, the phases of the moon and the seasons are caused by Earth's harmonic motion. A grandfather clock uses harmonic motion to tell time. This Investigation explores harmonic motion with a pendulum. The concepts you learn with the pendulum will also apply to other harmonic motion.

Materials

- Physics Stand
- Timer and photogate
- Pendulum
- Meter stick

1 Make a pendulum

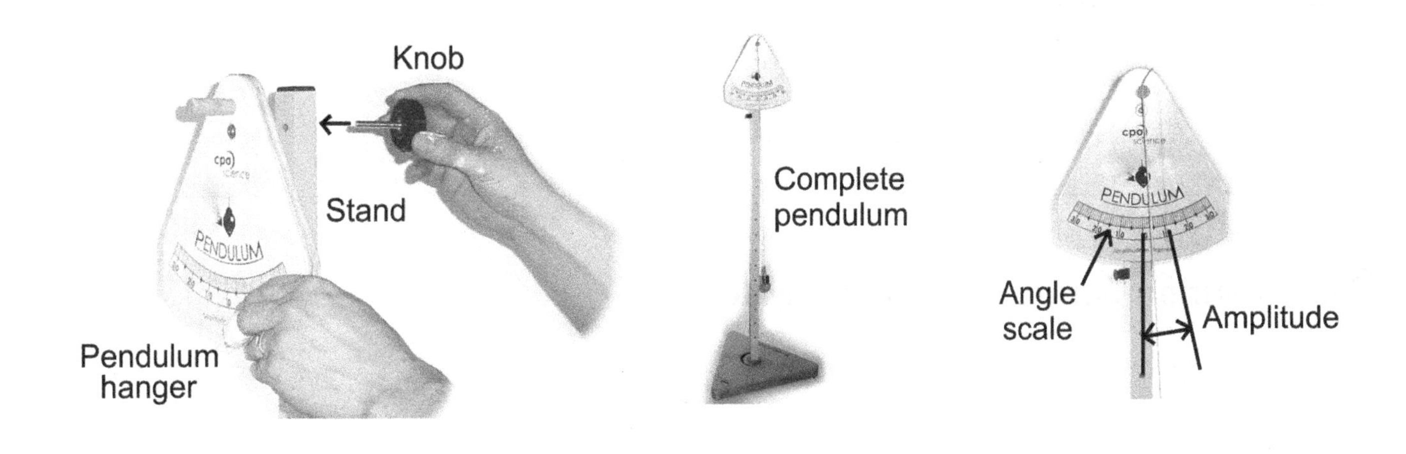

1. Put the pendulum together like it shows in the diagram.
2. Start the pendulum swinging and watch it for a minute. Think about how to describe the motion.

2 Thinking about what you observed

a. Write one sentence about the motion using the word "cycle."

b. The *amplitude* is the maximum amount the pendulum swings away from its resting position. The resting position is straight down. One way to measure amplitude is the angle the pendulum moves away from center. Write one sentence describing the motion of your pendulum using the word "amplitude."

c. Draw a sequence of sketches that describe one complete cycle using arrows to indicate the direction the pendulum is going at that point in the cycle.

3 Oscillators and period

1. Use the stopwatch to measure the period of your pendulum. Time ten cycles. Do three trials and use Table 1 to record your data.
2. Divide the average time for ten cycles by 10 to get the period.
3. Write a one sentence description of how you measured the period.

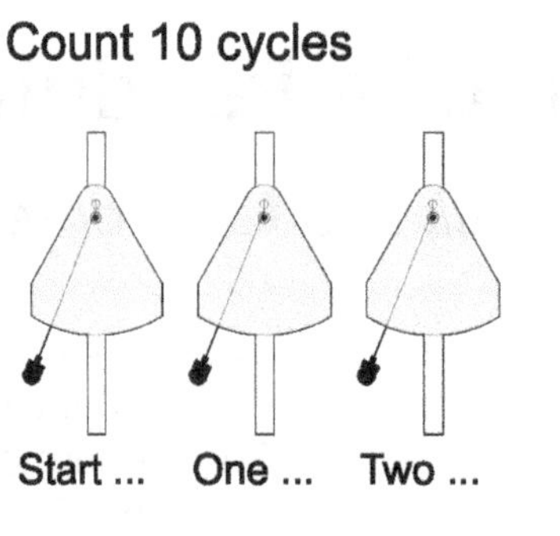

Divide time by 10

example
period = 15.20 sec ÷ 10
= 1.52 seconds

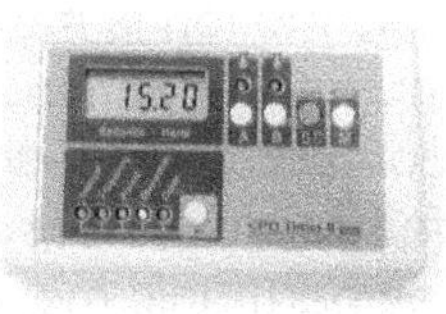

Timer in stopwatch mode

Table 1: Pendulum period data: Time for 10 cycles (sec)

Trial 1	Trial 2	Trial 3	Average
Period of pendulum (average divided by 10)			

4 Measuring period with a photogate

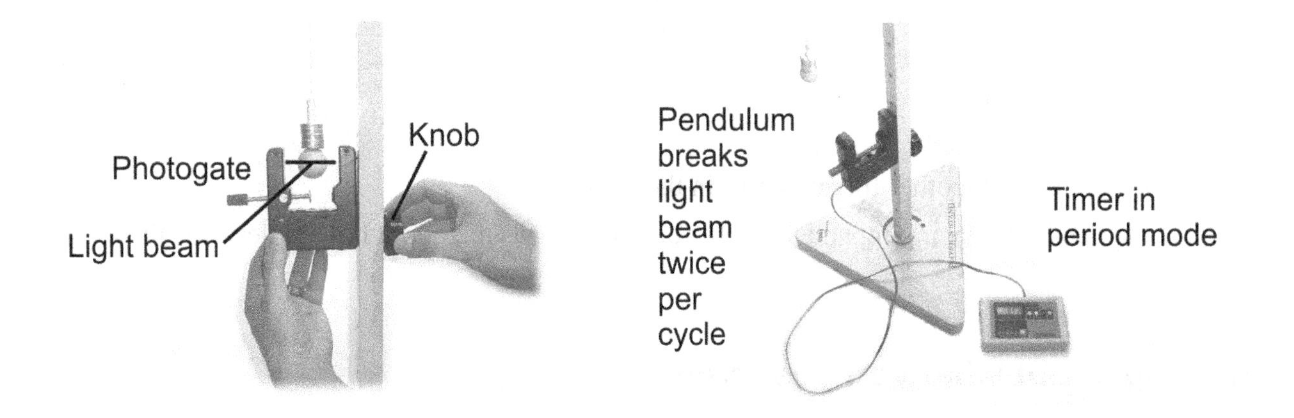

1. Attach the photogate as shown in the diagram. The pendulum breaks the light beam when it swings through the photogate. Try to keep the string length close to the length you used in part 2.
2. Put the Timer in period mode and let the pendulum swing through the light beam.
3. The reset (O) button does two things. If you press reset once, the display freezes, allowing you to write down a number before it changes. Pressing reset a second time starts another measurement.

5 Thinking about what you observed

a. Write down the time measurement you get from the Timer.

b. Is the time you get from the Timer the period of the pendulum? Explain why the time is or is not the period of the pendulum (hint: compare to your results from part 2).

c. Explain how the time measured by the Timer is related to the period of the pendulum.

6 What variables affect the period of a pendulum?

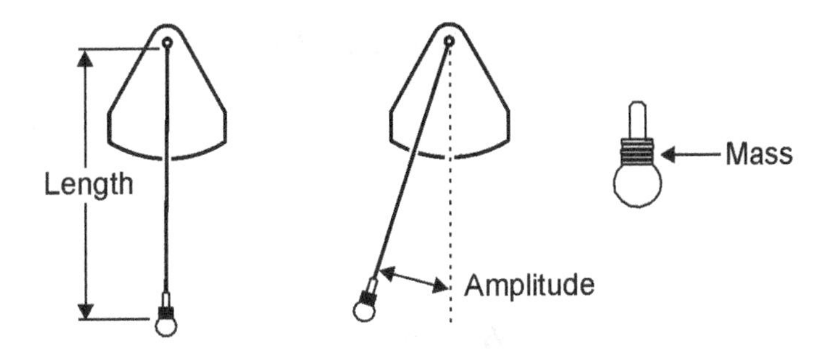

You can change several things about the pendulum.

- The amplitude (angle)
- The mass (add or subtract washers)
- The length of the string (measure as shown)

a. Think of three experiments you can do to see what variables affect the period of the pendulum. Write down one sentence describing each experiment.

b. Do the three experiments and record the measurements you make to assess the effect of changing each variable.

c. Write a sentence about the effect of each variable. Write a second sentence explaining how the data you took support the statement you made about each variable. For example,

"We found that changing _____ had almost no effect on the period. We know because when we changed _____ from _____ to _____ the period only changed from _____ to _____, which is a very small difference.

9B Waves

How do waves work?

Waves are oscillations that move from one place to another. Like oscillations, waves also have the properties of frequency and amplitude. In this investigation, you will explore waves on strings and in water. What you learn applies to all other types of waves as well.

Materials

- Metal Slinky® toy spring
- Meter stick
- A length of 1" plastic pipe cut to fit the wave tray
- Food coloring
- Water
- Wave tray with wooden blocks.

1 Making a wave pulse

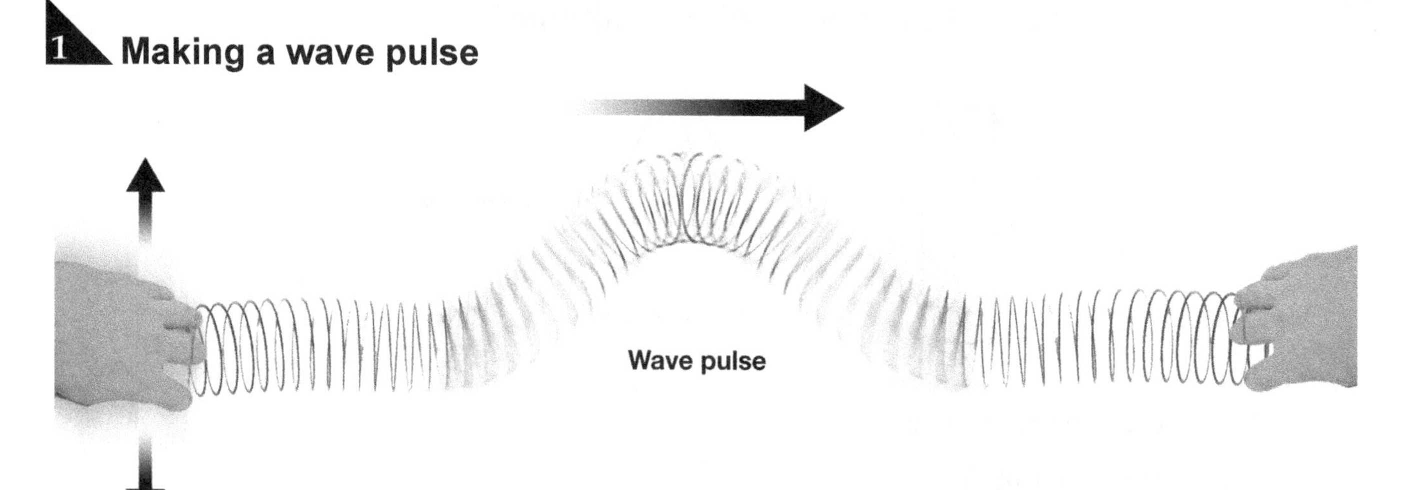

1. It takes two students to do this experiment. Each student takes one end of the spring.
2. Bring the spring down to the floor. Stretch it to a length of about 3 meters while keeping the spring on the floor.
3. One student should jerk one end of the spring rapidly to the side and back, just once. A wave pulse should travel up the spring.
4. Watch the wave pulse as it moves up and back. Try it a few times.

2 Thinking about what you observed

a. How is the motion of a wave pulse different from the motion of a moving object such as a car? (HINT: What is it that moves in the case of a wave?)

b. What happens to the wave pulse when it hits the far end of the spring? Watch carefully. Does the pulse stay on the same side of the spring or flip to the other side? Use the word "reflect" in your answer.

c. Imagine you broke the spring in the middle. Do you think the wave could cross the break? Discuss the reasoning behind your answer in a few sentences.

d. Why does the wave pulse move along the spring instead of just staying in the place you made it?

3 Waves in water

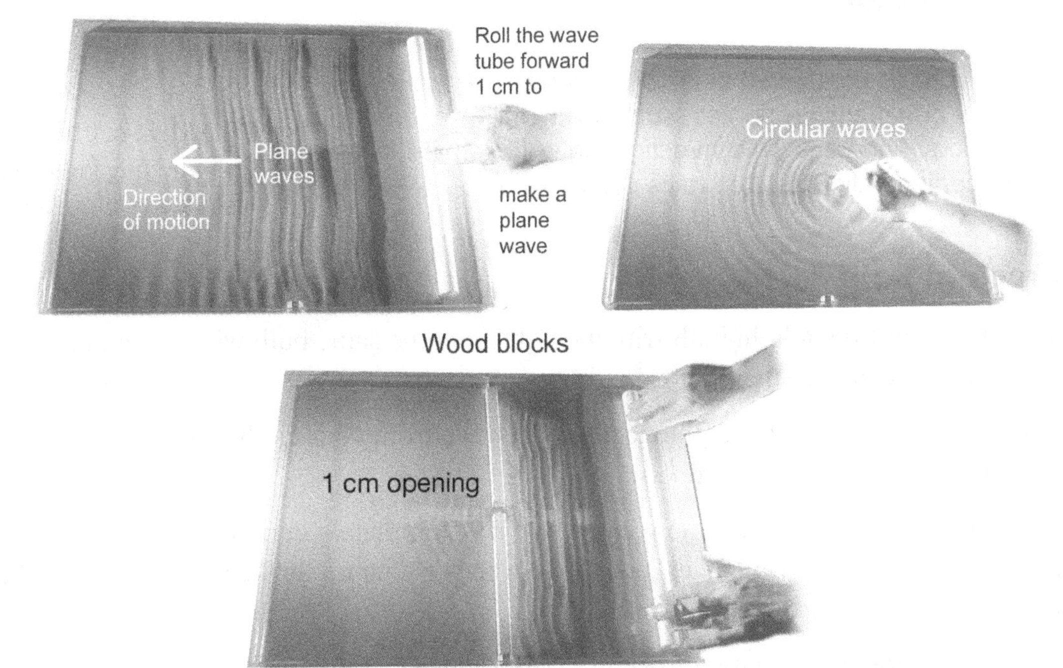

1. Fill a flat tray with about one-half centimeter of colored water. The color helps you see the waves.
2. Roll the wave tube forward about 1 cm in a smooth motion. This launches a nearly straight wave called a *plane wave* across the tray.
3. Next, poke the surface of the water with your fingertip. Disturbing a single point on the surface of the water makes a *circular wave* that moves outward from where you touched the water.
4. Arrange two wood blocks so they cross the tray leaving a 1 cm opening between them.
5. Make a plane wave that moves toward the blocks. Observe what happens to the wave that goes through the opening.

4 Thinking about what you observed

a. Draw a sketch that shows your plane wave from the top. Also on your sketch, draw an arrow that shows the direction the wave moves.

b. Is the wave parallel or perpendicular to the direction the wave moves?

c. Draw another sketch that shows the circular wave. Add at least four arrows that show the direction in which each part of the wave moves.

d. At every point along the wave, are the waves more parallel or perpendicular to the direction in which the circular wave moves?

e. Sketch the shape of the wave before and after passing through the 1 cm opening.

f. Does the wave change shape when it passes through the opening? If you see any change, your answer should state into what kind of shape the wave changes.

10A The Colors of Light

How is color created?

Light is so useful and so common that we often don't think about what light is. Light has many properties, such as its ability to carry images, colors, and heat. This investigation will examine some of the properties of light related to its color.

Materials

- CPO Light & Color
- Color mixing kit including magenta, yellow, and cyan clay

1 Sources of light

a. Compare the light from a light bulb with the light from the same bulb when seen in a mirror. In both cases, describe the path of the light from the source to your eyes.

b. Look at your clothes. Does the light reaching your eye from your clothes originate in your clothes? Or does the light originate somewhere else?

c. Turn off all the lights, and shade the windows so it is completely dark. Can you see your clothes in the dark? What does this experiment tell you about whether your clothes give off their own light or reflect light from somewhere else?

d. Turn on a television or computer screen in a dark room. Can you see the TV or computer screen in the dark? What does this experiment tell you about whether the TV or computer screen give off their own light or reflect light from somewhere else?

2 Mixing colors of light

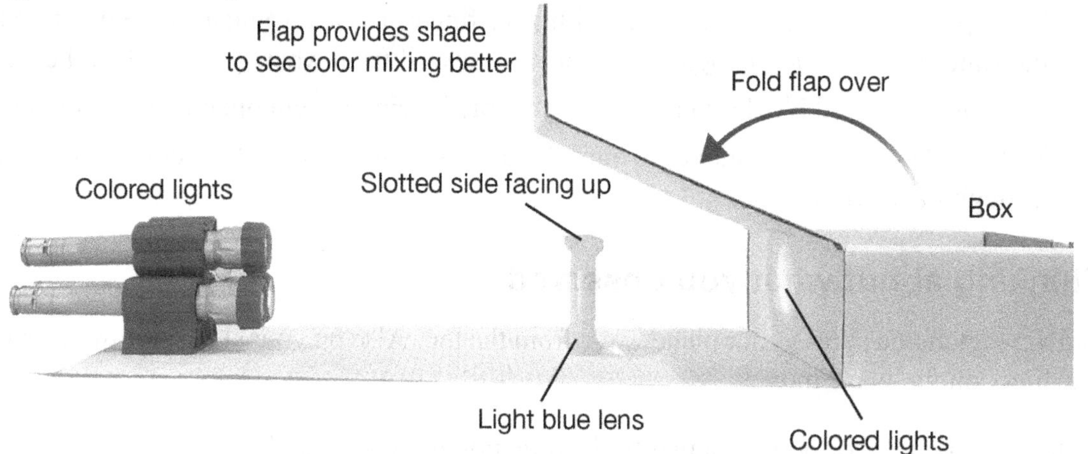

1. Slide all three flashlights into their own light stand. Connect the red and green flashlights by sliding their stands together using the rail and slot connectors on the side.
2. Set the blue flashlight on top of the other two with the stand on its side, so that the rail on the stand fits in the small groove created between the stands of the red and green lights.
3. Set the light blue lens just in front of the lights so they shine through it. Place the lens so the slotted side is pointing up.

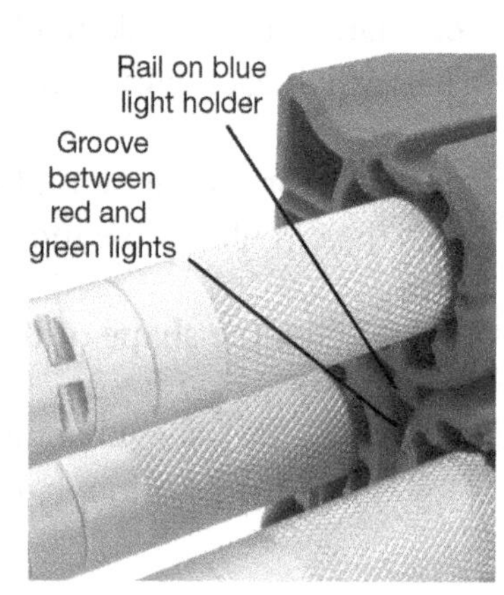

4. Set the Light & Color kit white box on opposite side of the paper from the lights. Fold the top of the box over to shade the three overlapping colored spots of light.
5. Slowly move the lens away from the lights and toward the box until the three spots of color are overlapped and in focus on the screen. Record the colors you see in Table 1.

Table 1: Mixing colors of light

Color combination	Color you see
Red + Green	
Green + Blue	
Blue + Red	
Red + Green + Blue	

3 The subtractive color model (CMYK)

1. You have three colors of clay: yellow, magenta, and cyan. Mix portions the size of your fingertip of the cyan and the magenta clay together. What color do you get?
2. Mix equal amounts of cyan and yellow. What color do you get?
3. Mix equal amounts of yellow and magenta. What color do you get?

The subtractive color model (CMYK)

	Cyan	Magenta	Yellow	Black
Absorbs	Red	Green	Blue	Red, Green, Blue
Reflects	Blue, Green	Blue, Red	Red, Green	None

Cyan Magenta Yellow

Mix equal amounts of the three subtractive primary colors
(two colors at a time)

4 Thinking about what you observed

a. Explain how the mixture of magenta and cyan makes its color when seen in white light.

b. Explain how the mixture of cyan and yellow makes its color when seen in white light.

c. Explain how the mixture of yellow and magenta makes its color when seen in white light.

d. Why don't the mixed colors produce full red, green, or blue?

e. What color would appear if you looked at a mixture of magenta and cyan under a lamp that only made blue light?

f. Research how printers make colors. Do they use red, green, and blue (RGB) or cyan, magenta, yellow, and black (CMYK)?

g. Research how computer monitors and televisions make colors. Do they use red, green, and blue (RGB) or cyan, magenta, yellow, and black (CMYK)? Explain why TV's and computer screens need to use one model or the other.

10B Magnification with a Lens

How does a magnifying glass work?

In optics, objects are real physical things that give off or reflect light rays. Images are "pictures" of objects that are formed where light rays meet. Images are created by mirrors, lenses, prisms, and other optical devices. This investigation will look at images produced by lenses.

Materials

- White paper
- Magnifying lens
- Ruler
- Graph paper
- Lamp or sunlit area
- Meter stick

1 Focusing light

A lens is a shaped and polished object that bends (refracts) light. Most lenses are made of transparent glass or plastic.

1. Use the magnifying glass to focus light from a lamp or the sun into a bright spot, like in the picture.
2. Complete the diagram to the right to show what happens to the light rays after they pass through the lens. Do they bend or continue moving straight?

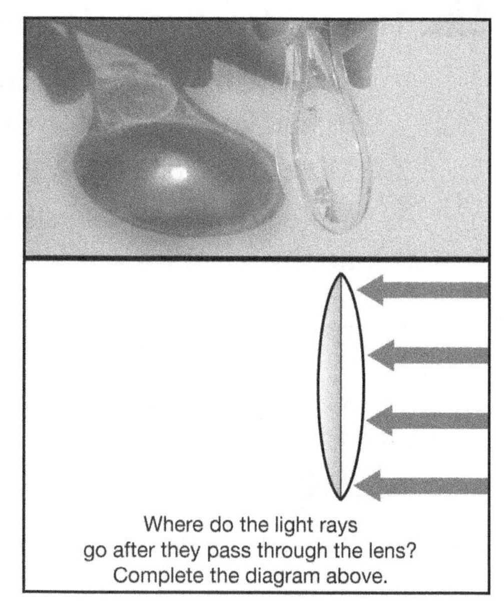

Where do the light rays go after they pass through the lens? Complete the diagram above.

2 Making an image with a lens

A single lens makes an image of a distant light source. The image forms one focal length away from a lens.

1. Find a wall at least 5 meters away from a lamp or sunlit window. Tape a piece of white paper to the wall to create a screen for seeing the image.
2. Hold the lens at different distances from your screen. Try distances between 10 and 30 cm.
3. You will see a sharp image of the lamp or window on the screen when your lens is about one focal length away from the wall.

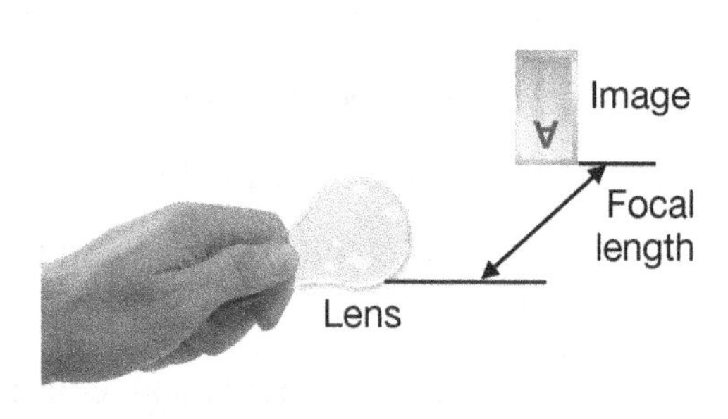

3 Stop and think

Images can be smaller or larger than the object that created them. Images can also be right side up or inverted.

a. Was the image created by a single lens smaller or larger than the object?

b. Was the image right side up or was it inverted?

Object: For this example the letter A was taped on a flourescent light fixture

4 Finding the magnification of a lens

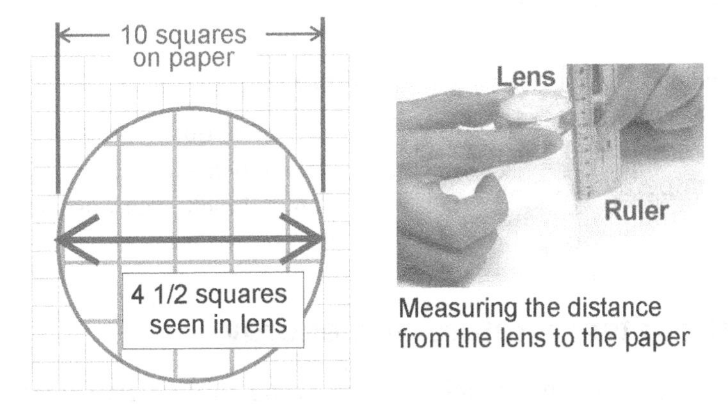

Measuring the distance from the lens to the paper

1. Take one of the lenses and set it on a piece of graph paper. Count the number of *unmagnified* squares that cross the diameter of the lens. In the example, the lens is 10 squares wide.
2. Look at the graph paper through the lens held above the paper at different distances. Move the lens until you have the biggest squares you can see clearly in the lens.
3. Count the number of *magnified* squares that cross the diameter of the lens. For example, the picture shows 4 1/2 squares across the lens.
4. The magnification is the number of *unmagnified* squares divided by the number of *magnified* squares. In the example, there are 10 *unmagnified* squares and 4.5 *magnified* squares. The magnification is $10 \div 4.5$, or 2.22.
5. Try the experiment again using a ruler to measure the distance between the lens and the paper. Notice that the magnification changes with different distances.

Table 1: Magnification data for a single lens

Distance to paper (cm)	# of squares on the graph paper (unmagnified squares)	# of squares in the lens (magnified squares)	Magnification

5 Thinking about what you observed

a. Is the image in a magnifying glass inverted or upright?

b. At what distances will the lens act like a magnifying glass? What happens when the object is more than a focal length away?

c. Describe something that looks completely different under a magnifying glass than when seen with the un-aided eye.

11A Temperature and Heat

How are temperature and heat related?

Hot and cold are familiar sensations. This investigation will explore the concept of temperature and also the difference between temperature and thermal energy (heat).

Materials

- Digital thermometer 0-100°C
- Digital balance
- Ten 1/2 inch-steel washers
- Stirrer
- Foam cups with at least 200 mL capacity
- Ice
- Hot and cold tap water

1 Thinking about temperature and energy

Consider the following experiment (which you are going to do). Two foam cups contain equal masses of water. One cup contains cold water with a temperature of 0°C. The other contains hot water with a temperature of 50°C. The hot water is mixed with the cold water and stirred.

a. Which cup has more energy, the hot one or the cold one? Why do you think so?

b. What do you think the temperature of the mixture will be? Why?

c. If the system includes both the cold and hot water, compare the energy of the system before mixing to the energy after mixing. Ignore any energy going to air or friction.

2 Doing the experiment

1. Prepare foam cups containing 100 g each of hot and cold water.
2. Measure and record the temperatures before mixing.
3. Mix the water, stir well, and measure the final temperature.

Table 1: Temperature data for mixing equal masses of water

Cold water temp. (°C)	Hot water temp. (°C)	Mixture temp. (°C)

3 Stop and think

a. Given the actual hot and cold temperatures, what do you think the mixture temperature should be?

b. Did the result of the experiment agree with your prediction? Discuss the meaning of "agree" in terms of the accuracy and precision of your experiment.

4 Doing an experiment with metal and water

Measure 100 - 125 grams of washers (cold)

1. Put enough washers in a foam cup so the mass is between 100 and 150 grams. Record the mass of the washers.
2. Prepare an equal mass of hot water in another foam cup.
3. Cover the washers with ice and water so they become cold.
4. Record the temperature of the cold water and washers, then pour off all the water *leaving just the washers in the cup.*
5. Add the equal mass of hot water to the cup with the washers.
6. Mix the water and washers, stir well, and measure the final temperature.

Table 2: Temperature data for combining water and steel washers

Washer Mass (g)	Washer temp. before mix (°C)	Hot water mass (g)	Hot water temp. before mix (°C)	Mixture temp. (°C)

5 Stop and think

a. Why didn't the temperature of the steel and water mixture come out halfway between cold and hot, even though you mixed equal masses? (Hint: heat is a form of energy that is proportional to temperature)

b. Heat is another word for thermal energy. Different materials *at the same temperature* can contain different amounts of heat. Research and describe the property of a material that measures its ability to store heat. What units does this property have?

c. How much energy does it take to raise the temperature of a kilogram of steel by 1 °C compared to raising the temperature of 1 kg of water the same amount?

11B Phase Change and Energy

What happens to heat and temperature when ice changes to water?

We experience matter in three phases: solid, liquid, and gas. Changing from one phase to another means changing the bonds between atoms therefore energy must either be used or given off. This investigation will explore how much energy it takes to change matter from one phase to the next.

Materials

- Digital thermometer 0-100°C
- Digital scale
- Stirrer
- Foam cups with at least 200 mL capacity
- Ice
- Hot and cold tap water

1 Doing the experiment

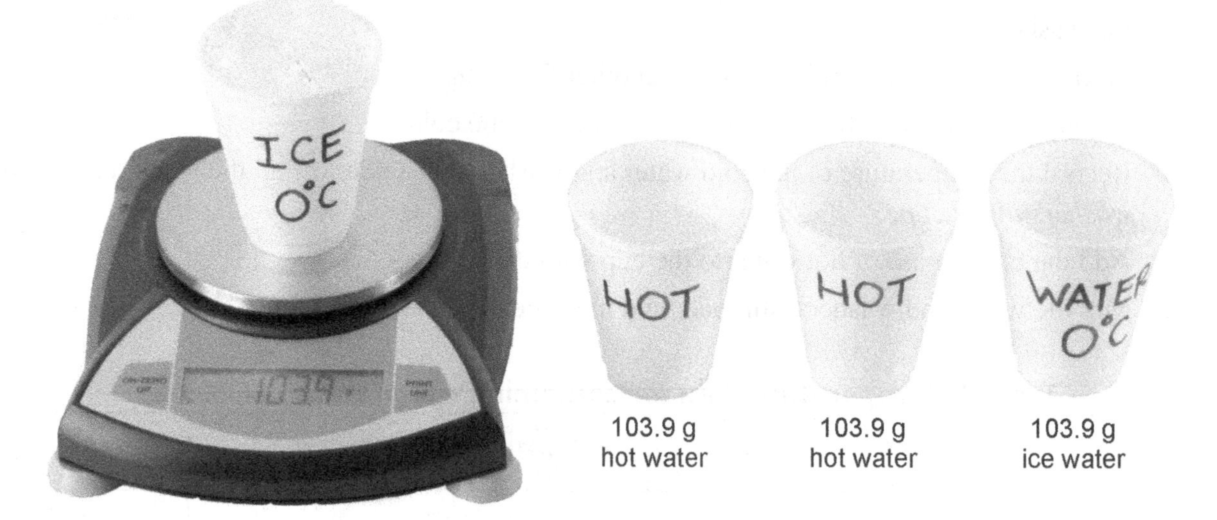

Measure equal masses into all four cups
(103.9 g is example only, use your own mass)

1. Place some crushed ice in cold water, then scoop at least 100 g of ice into a foam cup. Try not to get any liquid water, just ice.
2. Measure the mass of the ice and cup.
3. Make another cup with an equal mass of cold ice water (with ice removed).
4. Make two cups with an equal mass of hot water.
5. Measure and record the temperatures before mixing. Assume the solid ice is at 0°C.
6. Mix the ice and hot water in one cup. Stir well, and measure the final temperature after all the ice has melted.
7. Mix the hot and cold water in another cup. Stir well, and measure the final temperature.

Table 1: Temperature data for mixing equal masses of water

Liquid cold water plus hot water		
Cold water temperature before mixing (°C)	**Hot water temperature before mixing (°C)**	**Mixture temperature (°C)**
Solid water (ice) plus hot water		
Ice temperature before mixing (°C)	**Hot water temperature before mixing (°C)**	**Mixture temperature (°C)**
0		

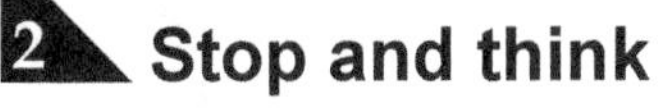

Stop and think

a. Given the actual hot and cold temperatures, what do you think the mixture temperature should have been if the ice could change to liquid (of the same temperature) without any change in energy?

b. Was the final temperature of the ice + water mixture about the same, more, or less than the final temperature of the water + water mixture?

c. Explain the difference in temperatures using the concepts of energy and phase change (heat of fusion). You may refer to the following diagram.

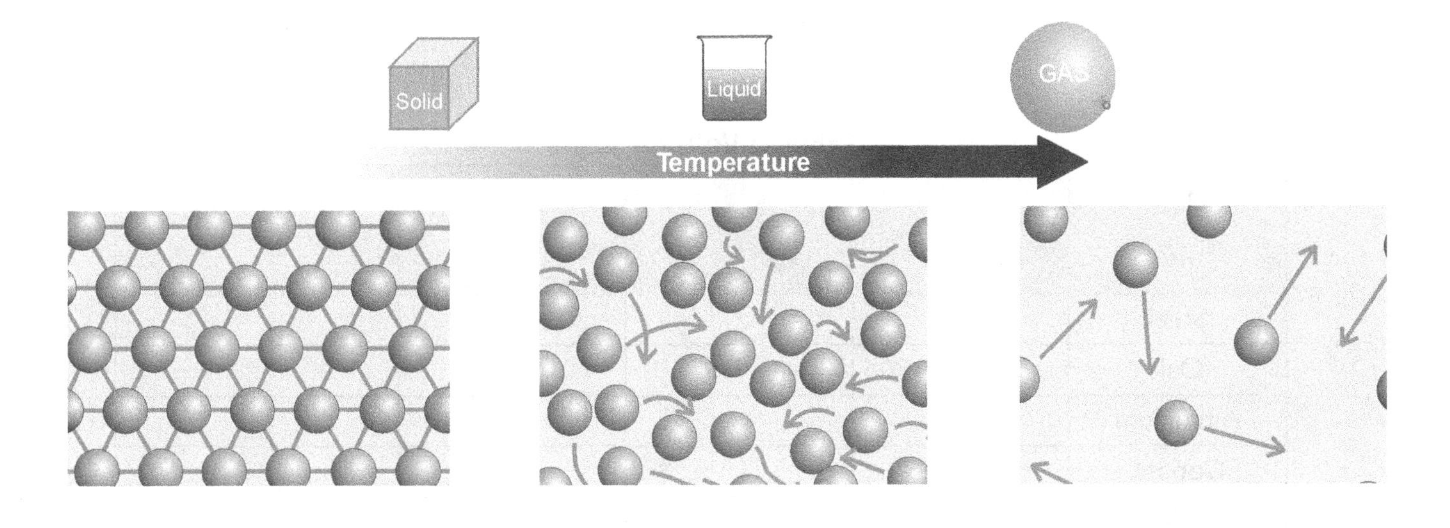

A challenging question

a. Use the data you have to estimate how much energy is required to change one kilogram of ice into one kilogram of liquid water at the same temperature. This energy is called the heat of fusion (for water).

12A Density

How does density determine if an object floats or sinks?

Things that are the same size don't usually have the same mass. Mass depends on both volume and density. Density is a property of solids, liquids, and gases. In this investigation, you will determine the densities of different materials. Based on the density, you will predict which ones float and which ones sink in water.

Materials

- Displacement tank
- Density cubes
- Digital balance
- Metric ruler
- 100-milliliter graduated cylinder
- A 250-milliliter beaker
- Water
- Paper towels
- Disposable cup

1 Measuring volume

1. Use the method demonstrated in the diagram on the right to measure the length, width, and height of the steel cube, in centimeters.
2. Record your measurements in Table 1.
3. Calculate the volume of the steel cube; Volume = length x width x height
4. Record your volume calculations in cubic centimeters in Table 1.
5. Repeat steps 1 - 5 for the other 4 cubes.

Table 1: Volume Table

Material of solid cube	Length (cm)	Width (cm)	Height (cm)	Volume from calculation (cm^3)
Steel				
Oak				
Aluminum				
Copper				
PVC				

Calculating the density

Each cube's volume is almost exactly the same, but their masses are different because they are all made of different materials. Use Table 2 to calculate the density of each cube.

1. Use a balance to determine the mass of the steel cube, and record it in Table 2.
2. Divide the mass by the volume of the steel cube to calculate its density: Density (g/cm^3) = mass (g) / volume (cm^3). Record the density value in Table 2.
3. Repeat steps 1 and 2 and calculate the density of each cube.

Table 2: Density data

Material of solid cube	Mass (g)	Volume (cm^3)	Density (g/cm^3)	Prediction (sink or float)	Result (sink or float)
Steel					
Oak					
Aluminum					
Copper					
PVC					

3 Stop and think

a. How do the volumes compare to each other? Why do you think they might be different?

b. Pick up and hold each cube. Predict whether it will sink or float in water. Record your predictions in Table 2. What did you base your predictions on?

c. What is the density of water in g/cm^3?

d. Compare the density of water to the density you calculated for each cube. Take another look at your sink/float predictions. Make any changes you need to based on density.

e. What rule did you use to make your prediction? Write the rule down in one sentence.

4 Testing the hypothesis

Your predictions from part 3d, and the rule from part 3e, represent a hypothesis. Test the hypothesis by dropping each cube in a beaker of water. Record your results in Table 2.

5 Thinking about what you observed

a. Describe in one sentence how to find the density of a regularly-shaped object like a cube.

b. Explain why these cubes have similar volumes but different masses.

c. Which method of prediction was better, testing the weight of the cube in your hand, or comparing the density of the cube to the density of water? Why?

d. **Challenge:** Can you use the displacement tank to measure the volume of a cube?

- Place a cup under the spout of the tank to catch any overflow of water.
- Fill the tank up until water just begins to run out of the spout. When it stops remove the cup and place a dry beaker under the spout.
- Place a cube in the tank. Measure the water that flows out of the spout. What did you get?
- Repeat the experiment, but place 5 cubes in the tank all at once. Try not to splash!
- What do you have to do to find the average volume of a single cube?

12B Sink or Float

Steel is denser than water, so why do steel boats float?

Solid objects float if they are less dense than the liquid in which they are placed. Objects sink if they are more dense than the liquid. You may have noticed that large ships are often made of steel. Steel is much denser than water. So how does a steel boat float? The answer is in the concept of *apparent density*. You will soon discover how and why boats can be made of materials that are denser than water.

Materials

- 1/2 stick of modeling clay
- Digital scale
- Displacement tank
- Disposable cup
- Beaker
- Graduated cylinder
- Container for testing boats (at least 15 cm deep)
- Water
- Paper towels

1 The density of clay

Find the density of your stick of clay before you change its shape.

1. Measure the clay's mass. Record it in Table 1.
2. Find the volume of your stick of clay using the displacement method:
   - Place a disposable cup under the displacement tank spout.
   - Fill the tank until water begins to run out of the spout (approx. 1,800 mL)
   - When the water stops flowing, remove the cup and replace it with a dry beaker.
   - Gently place your clay into the tank. Collect the water that runs out of the spout.
   - Quickly remove your clay and dry it with a paper towel. Do not allow water to mix with your clay or it will get very slimy.
   - The volume of the water you collected is equal to the volume of your clay. Use the graduated cylinder to measure the volume and record it in Table 1.

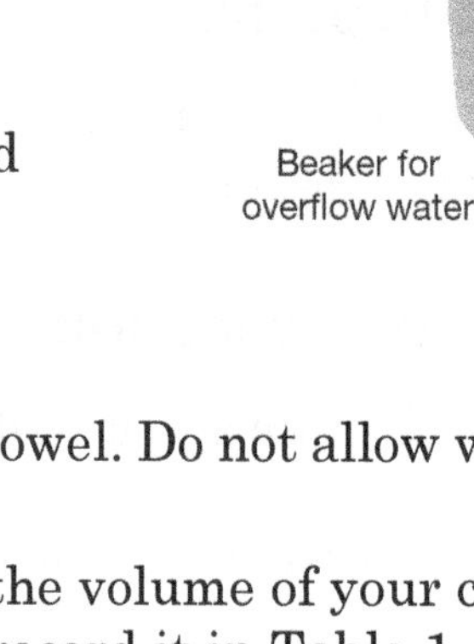

Table 1: Density data for clay

Substance	Mass (g)	Volume (mL)	Density (g/mL)
Clay			

3. Calculate the density in g/ml.
4. Did your stick of clay sink or float in the displacement tank? Use the density of your stick of clay and the density of water (1.0 g/mL) to explain why.

2 Making the clay float

You know that steel can be formed into a shape that floats. Can you do the same thing with clay? For this activity, you must use ALL of your clay. Mold it into a shape that you think will float.

1. Fill the container with water until it is about 12 centimeters deep.
2. When you are ready to test a shape that you have made, gently place it in the water in the container. If the clay sinks, take it out of the water and dry it off right away.
3. When your clay is dry, change the shape of your "boat" and try again.
4. When you have successfully made a boat that floats, take it out of the water. Dry it with a paper towel.
5. Measure the mass of your boat and record it in Table 2.

3 Why a boat floats

1. When a boat floats, it displaces a certain volume of water. Make a prediction: Do you think your boat will displace more water, less water, or the same amount as your stick of clay?
2. To find out, first prepare the displacement tank just as you did in step 1. Pour enough water in the displacement tank to make it overflow. Allow the water to stop overflowing out of the tank. Remove the cup that was catching the overflow water. Place a dry beaker under the spout to catch the overflow water so you can measure how much water your boat displaces.
3. Place your clay boat in the water in the displacement tank. Let it float there while the water flows out.
4. Measure the volume of the water displaced by your clay boat. Record this volume in Table 2.
5. Use your mass and volume data to calculate the apparent density of your clay boat. This value is called the *apparent* density because the total volume of the floating boat is not displaced since it is not completely submerged.

Table 2: Data for boat

Mass of boat (g)	Volume of water displaced by the boat (mL)	Apparent density of the boat (g/mL)

4 Thinking about what you observed

a. Which displaced more water, the stick of clay or the floating clay boat?

b. Assuming the mass of the clay did not change, how do you explain the difference in the volumes displaced by the stick of clay and the clay boat?

c. Look at the boat's apparent density. Why is it different than the density of the stick of clay? What other substance has a density very similar to the boat's apparent density?

d. Explain why a solid stick of clay sinks but a clay boat can be made to float.

e. What would happen if you added "cargo," like pennies, to your boat? Is there a limit to how much mass you can add before the boat sinks? Does the volume of displaced water increase or decrease when the boat gets heavier? Why? Try the experiment.

13A The Atom

What is inside an atom?

We once believed that atoms were the smallest units of matter. Then it was discovered that there are even smaller particles inside atoms! The structure of the atom explains why nearly all the properties of matter we experience are what they are. This investigation will lead you through some challenging and fun games that illustrate how atoms are built from protons, neutrons, and electrons.

Materials

- Atom Building Game

1 Modeling an atom

In the atom game, colored marbles represent the three kinds of particles. Red or green marbles are protons, blue marbles are neutrons, and yellow marbles are electrons.

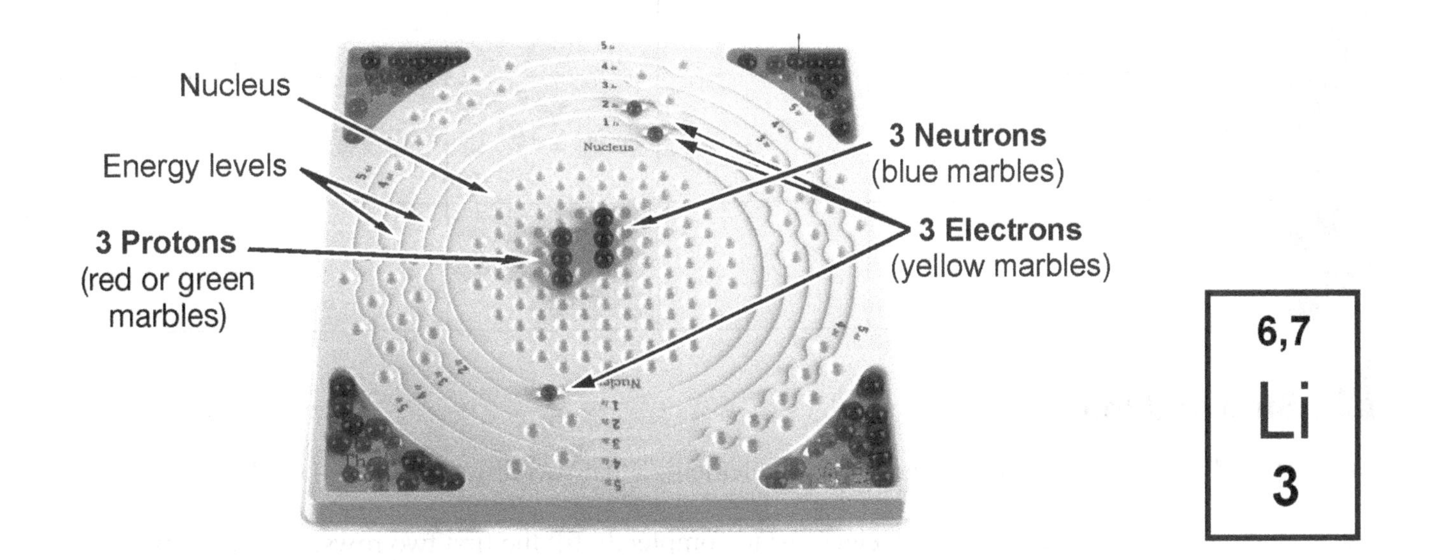

1. Build the atom above using three red or green, three blue, and three yellow marbles.

2 Thinking about the atom

a. What is the number below the element symbol? What does this number tell you about the the atom?

b. What is the number(s) above the element symbol called? What does this number tell you about the atom?

c. Why do some elements have more than one number above the symbol? What are the variations in this number called?

3 Making atoms

Build the 6 atoms shown on the chart and fill in the missing information Protons and neutrons go in the middle of the board. Electrons go in the outside and fill up the holes from the lowest row to the highest.

	Element	Atomic number	Mass number	Protons	Neutrons	Electrons
3a						
3b						
3c						
3d		8				
3e						
3f			27			

4 Stop and think

a. Two of the atoms you made were the same element. What was different about them?

b. One of the atoms had just enough electrons to completely fill the first two rows. Which atom was this? Where on the periodic table is it found?

c. Which atom had an atomic number of 8?

d. Which atom had a mass number of 14?

e. One atom is found in a lightweight, silvery metal used in airplanes. Which atom was it?

f. One atom represents an element that makes up about 21% of the air you breathe. You could not live without this element.

Periodic Table of the Elements 1- 54

(Stable isotopes)

Key: Element Symbol (Mo) · Atomic Number (42) · Stable Mass Numbers (92, 94-100)

1,2 **H** **1**																	3,4 **He** **2**
6,7 **Li** **3**	9 **Be** **4**											10,11 **B** **5**	12,13 **C** **6**	14,15 **N** **7**	16-18 **O** **8**	19 **F** **9**	20-22 **Ne** **10**
23 **Na** **11**	24-26 **Mg** **12**											27 **Al** **13**	28-30 **Si** **14**	31 **P** **15**	32-34, 36 **S** **16**	35,37 **Cl** **17**	36,38, 40 **Ar** **18**
39,41 **K** **19**	40,42-44,46, 48 **Ca** **20**	45 **Sc** **21**	46-50 **Ti** **22**	51 **V** **23**	50, 52-54 **Cr** **24**	55 **Mn** **25**	54,56-58 **Fe** **26**	59 **Co** **27**	58,60-62,64 **Ni** **28**	63,65 **Cu** **29**	64,66-68,70 **Zn** **30**	69,71 **Ga** **31**	70,72-74,76 **Ge** **32**	75 **As** **33**	74,76-78,80, 82 **Se** **34**	79,81 **Br** **35**	78,80, 82-84, 86 **Kr** **36**
85 **Rb** **37**	84, 86-88 **Sr** **38**	89 **Y** **39**	90-92, 94,96 **Zr** **40**	93 **Nb** **41**	92, 94-100 **Mo** **42**	none **Tc** **43**	96,98-103,104 **Ru** **44**	103 **Rh** **45**	102,104-106,108, 110 **Pd** **46**	107,109 **Ag** **47**	106,108, 110-112, 114,116 **Cd** **48**	113 **In** **49**	112,114-120,122, 124 **Sn** **50**	121 **Sb** **51**	120,122, 124-126, 128,130 **Te** **52**	127 **I** **53**	124,126, 128-132, 134,136 **Xe** **54**

13B Building the Elements

How were the elements created?

During the middle ages, people believed you could turn lead into gold if you followed the right procedures. Later, we learned that lead and gold are different elements with different kinds of atoms. You have to change the atoms inside to make lead into gold. Lead atoms have 82 protons in the nucleus. Gold atoms have 79 protons.

Materials

- Atom Building Game

1 Building the elements

About 13 billion years ago, when the universe was much younger, the only atoms in existence were hydrogen, helium, and a small amount of lithium. These are the three lightest elements. Today, we find carbon, oxygen, iron, and even uranium atoms. Where did these heavy atoms come from? All the elements were created in the super-hot cores of stars. Stars get their energy by combining hydrogen atoms together to make other elements, such as helium. Along the way, a few protons get converted to neutrons and electrons, too.

2 Quick review of the atom

In the atom game, colored marbles represent the three kinds of particles. Red or green marbles are protons, blue marbles are neutrons, and yellow marbles are electrons.

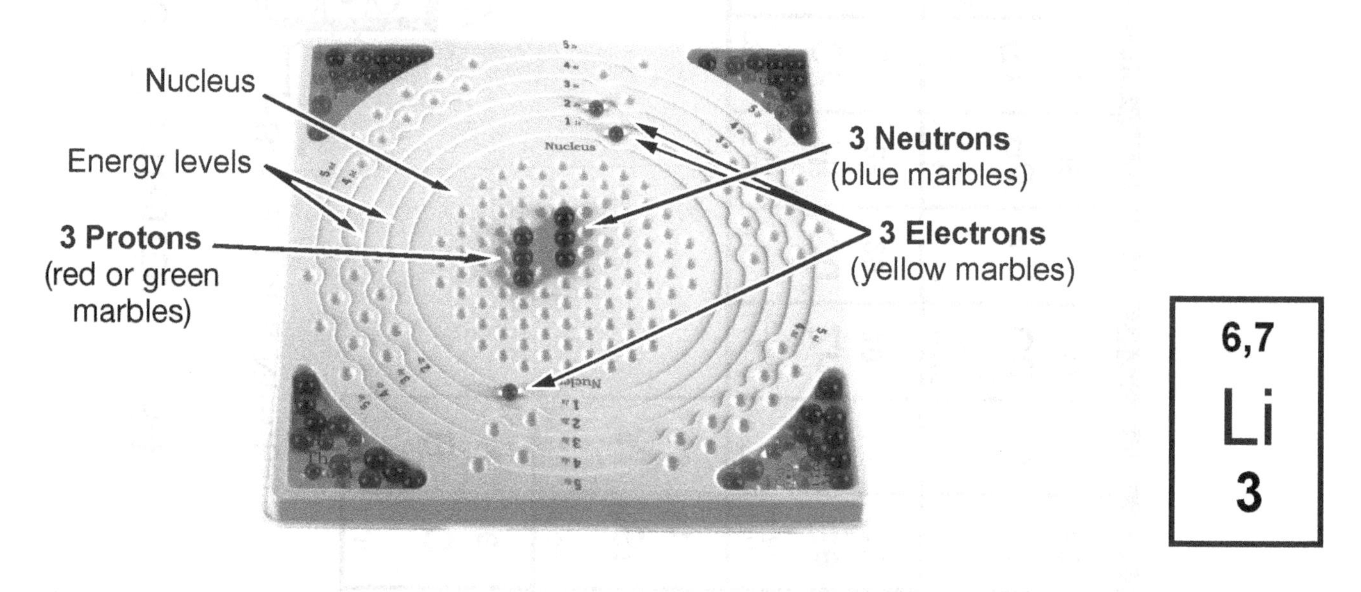

The Three Rules

Rule #1: The number of protons matches the atomic number

Rule #2: The total number of protons and neutrons equals a stable mass number

Rule #3: The number of electrons matches the number of protons

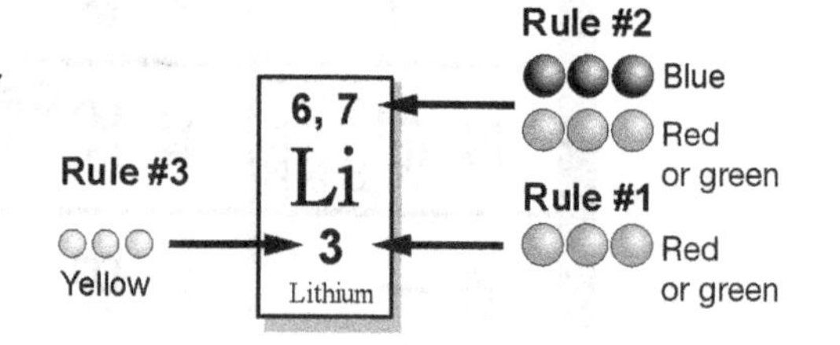

3 The game of atomic challenge

This game simulates how the heavy elements were created inside stars. Each player takes a turn adding protons, neutrons, and electrons to the atom to build heavier and heavier elements.

1. The winner of the game is the first player to run completely out of marbles.
2. Each player should start with 6 blue marbles (neutrons), 5 red or green marbles (protons), and 5 yellow marbles (electrons).
3. Each player takes turns adding 1 - 5 marbles, but not more than 5. The marbles may include any mixture of electrons, protons, and neutrons.
   FOR EXAMPLE: you can add one blue, one red or green, and one yellow marble in a turn. That makes three total marbles, which is less than 5.
4. Marbles played in a turn are added to the marbles already in the atom.
5. Only atoms where the electrons, protons, and neutrons match one of the naturally occurring elements on the table are allowed. If you add marbles that make an atom NOT on the red periodic table you have to take your marbles back and lose your turn.

Example of a good move

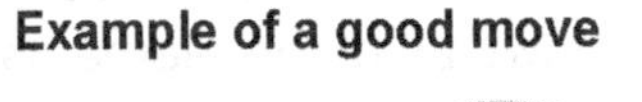

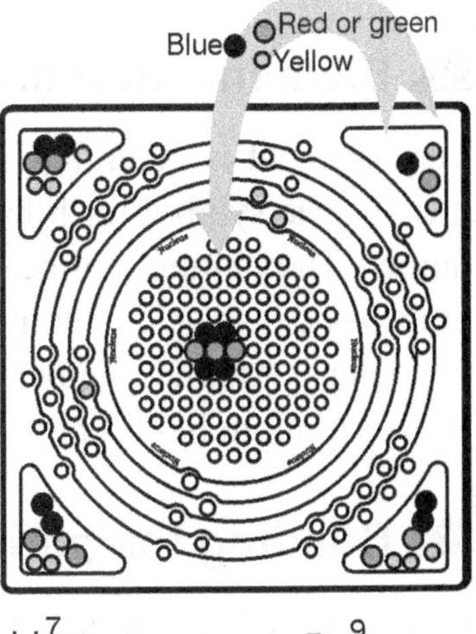

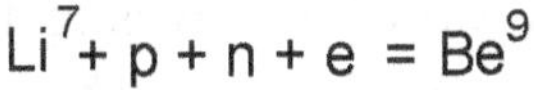

6. A player can trade marbles with the bank INSTEAD of taking a turn. The player can take as many marbles, and of as many colors as they need but must take at least as many total marbles as they put in. For example, a player can trade 2 yellows for 1 yellow, 1 blue, and 1 red or green.

4 Stop and think

Atoms which are not on the periodic table shown may exist in nature but they are radioactive and unstable. For example, carbon-14 (C^{14}) is unstable and is not listed although C^{12} and C^{13} are stable.

a. What four elements make up almost all of the mass in your body?

b. How many stable isotopes does oxygen have?

c. Find one element on the chart that has no stable isotopes.

d. What element has atoms with 26 protons in the nucleus?

e. On most periodic tables, a single atomic mass is listed instead of the mass numbers for all the stable isotopes. How is this mass related to the different isotopes?

14A The Periodic Table

What is the periodic table and how many elements are there?

Virtually all the matter you see is made up of combinations of elements. Scientists know of 118 different elements, of which about 90 occur naturally. Each element has its own unique kind of atom. The periodic table is a chart that shows all of the elements in order of increasing atomic number.

Materials

- Periodic Table Tiles

1 Elements and the atomic number

Every element is given a symbol of one or two letters. For example, the symbol for hydrogen is a capital letter H. The symbol for lithium is two letters, Li. Each element also has a unique number called the atomic number. The atomic number is the number of protons in the nucleus of all atoms of that element. Atomic number one is the element hydrogen. Hydrogen is the lightest element known, since it only has one proton in the nucleus. Atomic number 92 is the element uranium which is one of the heaviest elements that occurs in nature. Uranium has 92 protons in its nucleus.

2 Building the periodic table

For this part of the investigation, you are going to build the entire periodic table of elements. The table has a very specific shape which corresponds to the chemical properties of the elements. All of the elements fill in this shape in order of their atomic number starting from the upper left-hand corner. As you build the table, be sure to follow the diagram below to get the right shape. Some of the squares have the atomic numbers of the elements shown to help you get the shape correct.

Building the Periodic Table

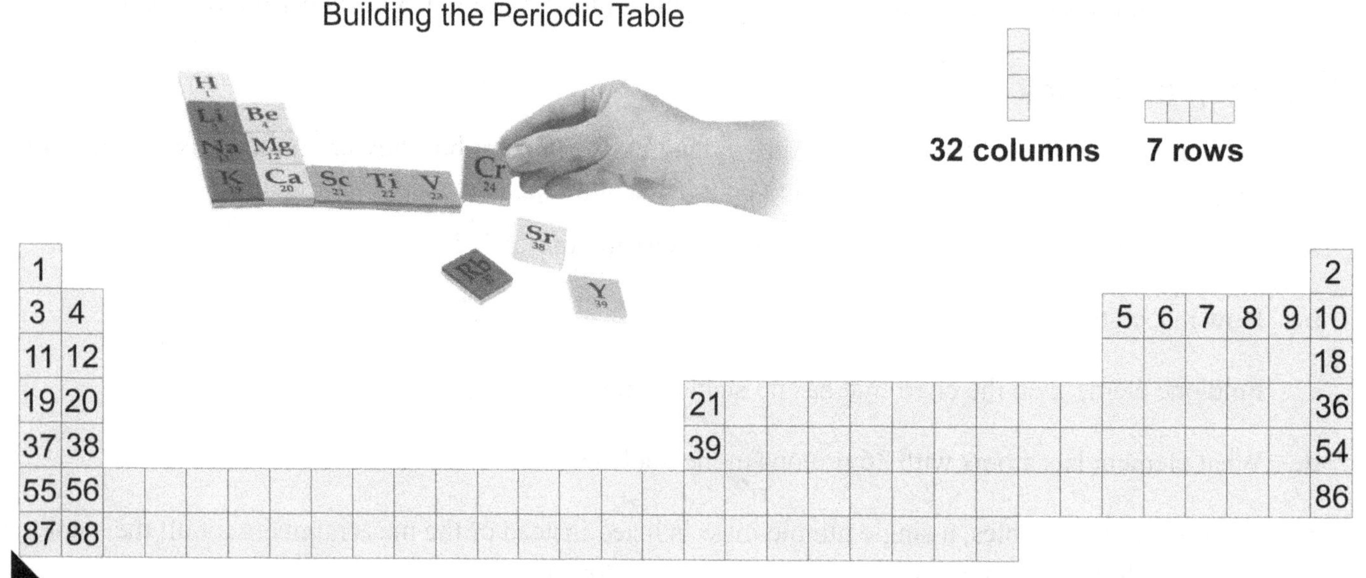

3 Stop and think

a. Many printed periodic tables look like the diagram on the right instead of having the shape that you built. Can you think of a reason why?

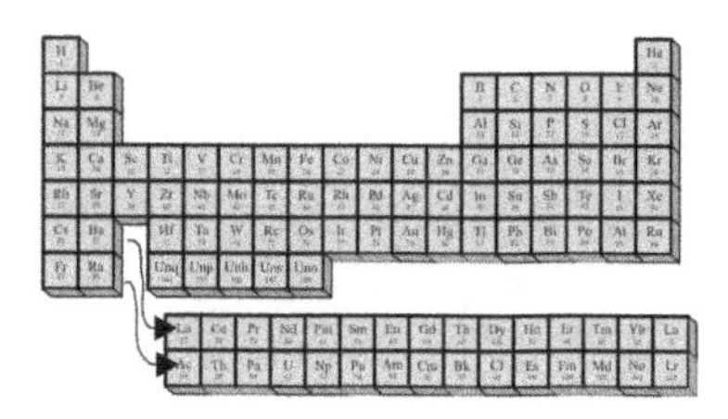

4 Sections of the periodic table

The periodic table is organized into 11 sections (shown as a-k). Each section contains elements with similar chemical properties. Most sections are single columns. One section includes many columns and two sections are parts of entire rows.

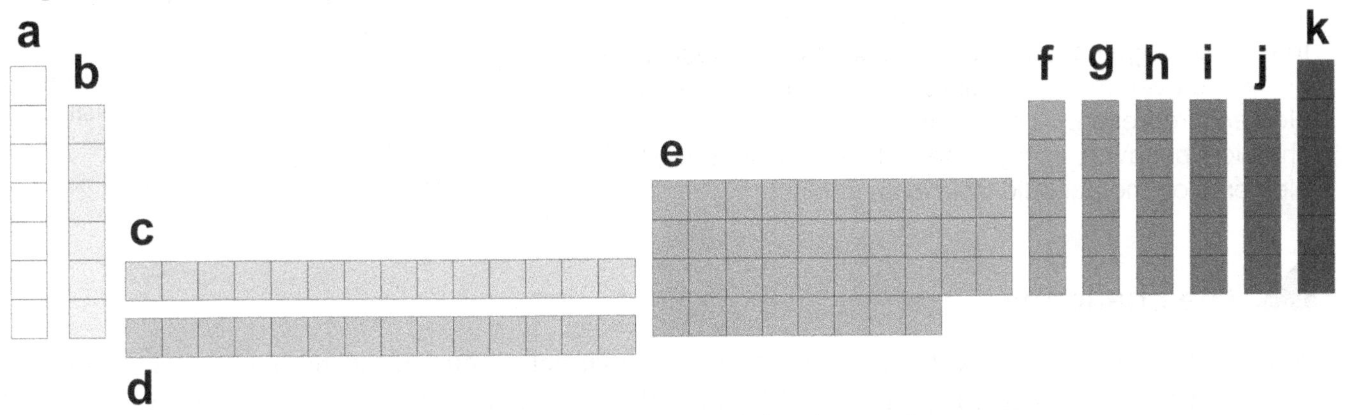

a. Locate the element that is the first one in each of the following sections.

b. Research the name (if any) of this section.

c. Research any properties that elements from this section share.

Table 1: Sections of the Periodic Table

Diagram	First element (name)	Section name (if any)	Representative chemical properties
a			
b			
c			
d			
e			
f			
g			
h			
i			
j			
k			

5 Applying what you have learned

a. Each row of the periodic table contains only a certain number of elements. What does this have to do with the structure of the atom? Research this question in your textbook.

b. Which section of the periodic table above contains the element argon? What characteristic do the elements in this section share?

c. Which section contains the element carbon? What characteristic do the elements in this section share?

14B Periodic Table Group Challenge

How is the periodic table organized?

Each box on the periodic table tells you the element symbol, atomic number, and atomic mass for all the known elements. This is very useful information, but did you know that the arrangement of the elements on the periodic table gives you even more information? Each major column of elements represents a group of elements with similar chemical behavior. Can you see why the arrangement of elements on the periodic table is important?

Materials

- Blank periodic table bingo card sheets; 1 per player
- Caller's clues and checklist; 1 per team
- Copy of the periodic table of elements; 1 per player
- Highlighter or other marker; 1 per player

1 The challenge

Periodic Table Group Challenge is a bingo-like game that helps you understand how the elements on the periodic table are arranged. Each player will fill out their own five-by-five grid with element symbols, and then the caller will read element clues. The players must interpret the clues and highlight any boxes on the grid that fit the clue. The first player that correctly highlights five boxes across, up-and-down, or diagonally in a row is the winner.

2 Rules of play

1. Designate one member of your group to be the caller. The caller will call out clues and keep track of them on the checklist.
2. Each player will have a sheet of 4 blank grids. Fill out one of the grids with random element symbols (other grids can be used for additional games). You may choose elements in the atomic number range of 1 – 54 (hydrogen through xenon). Do not repeat symbols on the card. You will only be able to fit 25 of the possible 54 symbols on the card. You choose which ones to use, and where to place them on the grid.
3. The caller will randomly pick clues from the list, and as a clue is called out, the caller will check off the clue. The answers are only for the caller to check the winner's card!
4. When a clue is called, players check the grid to see if any of the elements fit the clue. Any elements that fit the clue must be highlighted. If no elements fit the clue, then no boxes are highlighted on that turn.
5. When a player has five boxes highlighted in a row up and down, across, or diagonally, play stops. The caller will double check the clue list and answers to see if the clues indeed match the elements. Play continues until a true winner is determined.

3 Caller's clues

Clues can be called in any order. Check off each clue as you use it.

Clue	Possible Answers
A member of the carbon family	C, Si, Ge, Sn
Chemical properties similar to calcium, but not calcium	Be, Mg, Sr
A transition metal that has a "C" in the symbol	Sc, Cr, Co, Cu, Tc, Cd,
A member of the oxygen family	O, S, Se, Te
Chemical properties similar to cesium, but not cesium	H, Li, Na, K, Rb
A member of the noble gas family	He, Ne, Ar, Kr, Xe
A nonmetal in the nitrogen family	N, P
A metal in the boron family	Al, Ga, In
A gas in the oxygen family	O
A solid in the halogen family	I
An element that is liquid at room temperature	Hg, Br
A transition metal with less than 25 protons	Cr, V, Ti, Sc
A transition metal commonly found in jewelry	Ni, Cu, Ag
A metalloid in the carbon family	Si, Ge
Chemical properties similar to aluminum, but not aluminum	B, Ga, In
A transition metal with 39 – 43 protons	Y, Zr, Nb, Mo, Tc
An element symbol with a first letter that is different from the first letter of the name	Na, K, Fe, Ag, Sn, Sb
A member of the nitrogen family with a one-letter symbol	N, P
A transition metal from period 5	Y, Zr, Nb, Mo, Tc, Ru, Rh, Pd, Ag, Cd

4 Periodic table challenge card

Fill in each of the squares with the symbol of an element with atomic number between 1 and 54 (hydrogen - xenon)

You may not use the same element symbol twice.

15A Chemical Bonds

How do atoms form chemical bonds with other atoms?

Scientists have identified over 100 elements, but most matter found on Earth is not in the form of pure elements. Most matter is made up of compounds. Even if an element is pure at first, it will combine with other elements sooner or later. For example, if you leave an iron nail out in the rain, it will rust. The iron in the nail will combine with oxygen. It will form a compound called iron oxide, also known as rust. In this investigation, you will learn how electrons are involved in forming chemical bonds.

Materials

- 2 atom building games

1 Electrons in an atom

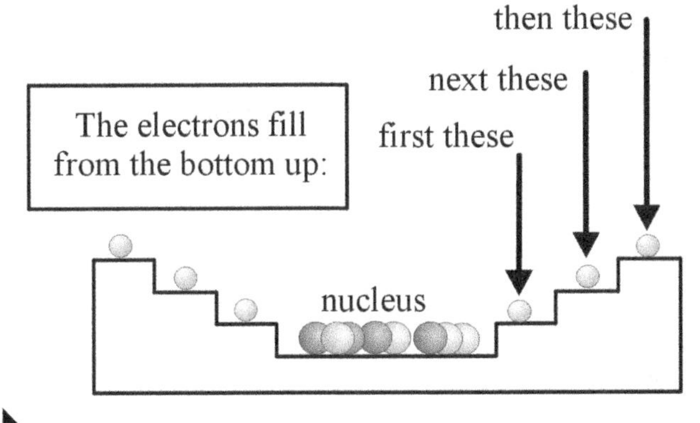

- A neutral atom has the same number of electrons and protons.
- The electrons move around in energy levels that surround the nucleus.
- Since electrons are attracted to the nucleus, they fill the levels closest to the nucleus first.
- Once a lower level is full, electrons start to fill the next level.

2 How many electrons are in the outermost level?

Use the atom board to make a model of each element in the table. For each element, write the number of electrons found in the outermost level. Then write the number of unoccupied or empty spaces in the outermost level.

Table 1: Electrons in the Outermost Levels of Atoms

Element	Atomic number	Electrons in outermost level	Unoccupied spaces in outermost level
hydrogen			
helium			
lithium			
fluorine			
neon			
sodium			
chlorine			
oxygen			
carbon			

a. What do lithium and sodium have in common?

b. What do fluorine and chlorine have in common?

c. What do neon and helium have in common?

3 Modeling a chemical bond

The following concepts will help you understand why and how atoms form chemical bonds.

- An atom has its lowest energy when its outermost energy level is either completely filled or completely empty.
- Atoms trade or share electrons to fill or empty their outermost energy level.
- Atoms form bonds by trading or sharing electrons from their outermost energy levels.
- Electrons in inner energy levels do not participate in bonding with other atoms.

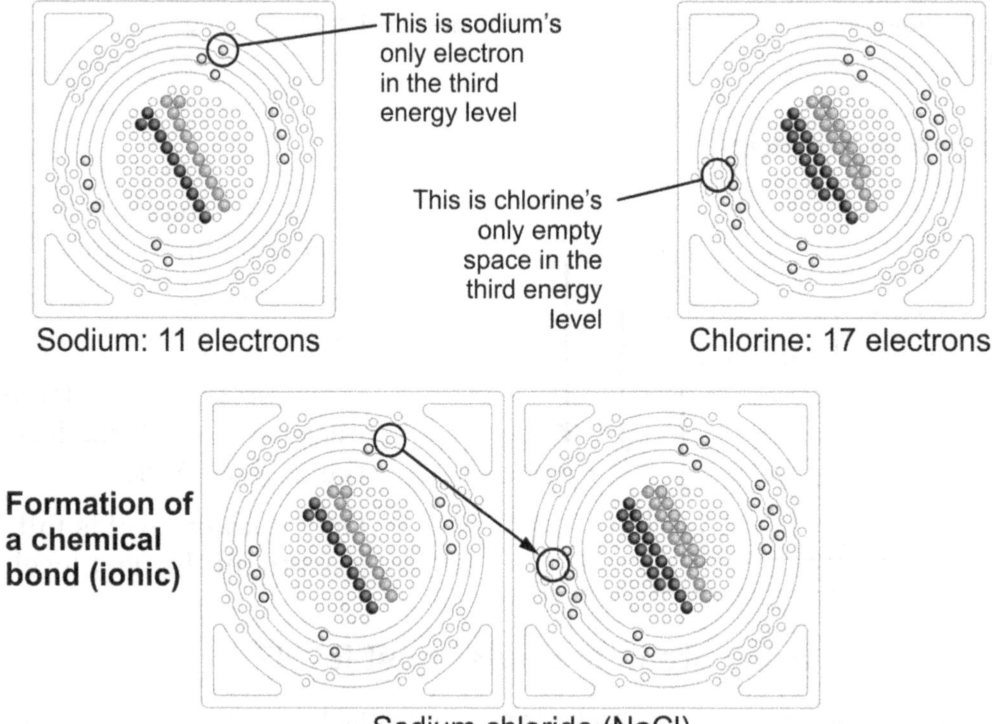

Use two atom boards and marbles. Build one sodium atom and one chlorine atom. Put them next to each other and answer the questions below.

a. A sodium atom has only one electron in its outermost level. What do you think it will do in order to complete that level? Do you think it will lose its outer electron? Or do you think it will gain seven electrons? Explain your answer.

b. Chlorine needs to complete its outermost energy level. Do you think chlorine will tend to lose all of its seven outer electrons? Or do you think it will gain one electron? Explain your answer.

c. What makes you think that sodium and chlorine might bond together? Describe what might happen if these two atoms form a chemical bond.

d. How many hydrogen atoms can bond with one oxygen atom? What chemical does this make?

e. How many chemical bonds can carbon form?

15B Molecules and Compounds

What are some molecules and compounds and what atoms are in them?

The properties of a material depend much more on the molecule than on the elements of which the molecule is made. For example, aspirin is made from carbon, hydrogen, and oxygen. By themselves, these elements do not have the property of reducing pain. Other molecules formed from the same elements have different properties than aspirin. For example, polyethylene plastic wrap and formaldehyde (a toxic preservative) are also made from carbon, oxygen, and hydrogen. The beneficial properties of aspirin come from the way the atoms bond together in the particular shape of the aspirin molecule.

Materials

- Periodic Table Tiles

1 Modeling compounds

In the previous investigation, you used the Atom Building Game board to model how sodium and chlorine combine to make the compound *sodium chloride*. In this investigation, we are going to model molecules and compounds by using the Periodic Table Tiles.

1. Find a tile that has the symbol for the element sodium on it.
2. Find a tile that has the symbol for the element chlorine on it.
3. Place these tiles next to each other, with their sides touching. You have just formed a unit of the compound called sodium chloride, which is common table salt. The chemical formula for sodium chloride is NaCl.

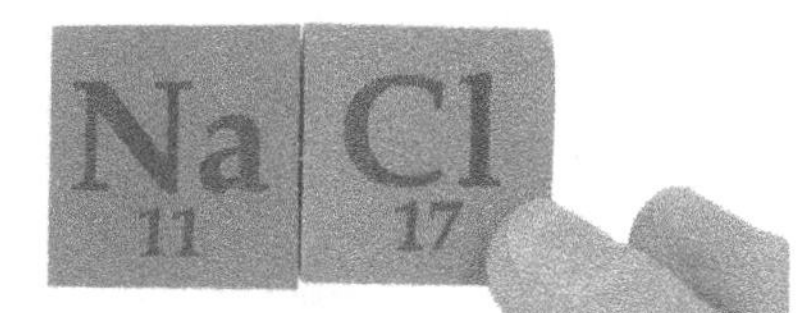

4. Find the correct tiles and model these compounds: LiCl and KCl.
5. Find the correct tiles and model these compounds: $CaCl_2$ and $MgCl_2$.

2 Stop and think

a. What does the small “2” in $CaCl_2$ and $MgCl_2$ tell you about the compounds?

b. Explain why the formulas $CaCl_2$ and $MgCl_2$ have a small “2” after the symbol for chlorine, but NaCl, LiCl, and KCl do NOT have this small “2” after the symbol for chlorine. (Hint: refer back to the previous investigation, where you counted the number of electrons in the outermost energy level for each type of atom.)

c. What do Li, K, and Na have in common? (Hint: refer to the periodic table of elements.)

d. What do Ca and Mg have in common? (Again, check out the periodic table of elements.)

e. The chemical name for NaCl is “sodium chloride”. Predict the names for LiCl and KCl.

f. The chemical name for $CaCl_2$ is “calcium chloride”. Predict the name for $MgCl_2$.

3 Fill in the missing information

Study the table below. Find the correct tiles to model each molecule as shown in the first row. After you have modeled each molecule, fill in the missing information.

Table 1:Modeling molecules

model	number of atoms	chemical formula	chemical name	common name
O 8 C 6 O 8	3	CO_2	carbon dioxide	carbon dioxide
O 8 S 16 O 8				sulfur dioxide
O 8 Si 14 O 8	3			silica (can be made as glass)
H 1 / H 1 C 6 H 1 / H 1			carbon tetrahydride	methane
C 6 O 8	2		carbon monoxide	carbon monoxide

4 Stop and think

a. Which of the molecules you just modeled is/are found in the emissions of power plants that burn fossil fuels like coal and oil?

b. Which molecule is a colorless, odorless gas that can be produced by a home furnace that isn't working properly? Special detectors are used to identify this potentially deadly gas.

c. You release this molecule from your lungs every time you breathe out.

d. This molecule is the main ingredient of natural gas, which can be used for home heating and cooking.

16A Solubility

What does it mean to dissolve?

The water you drink is not pure water. There are many things dissolved in drinking water, such as minerals, oxygen, and sometimes flavorings. A solution is a homogeneous combination of different compounds, such as water and sugar. Carbonated soda is a solution containing water, sugar, dissolved carbon dioxide gas, and flavorings. Solutions are essential for life because your body's chemical processes happen in solutions. This investigation will look at some of the properties of solutions.

Materials

- Graduated cylinder
- Digital scale
- Granulated sugar
- Hot water
- Cold water
- Sugar cubes
- Timer
- Stirring rod
- Water soluble markers: red and blue
- Two 100-mL beakers
- Two foam cups

1 Mass and volume in solutions

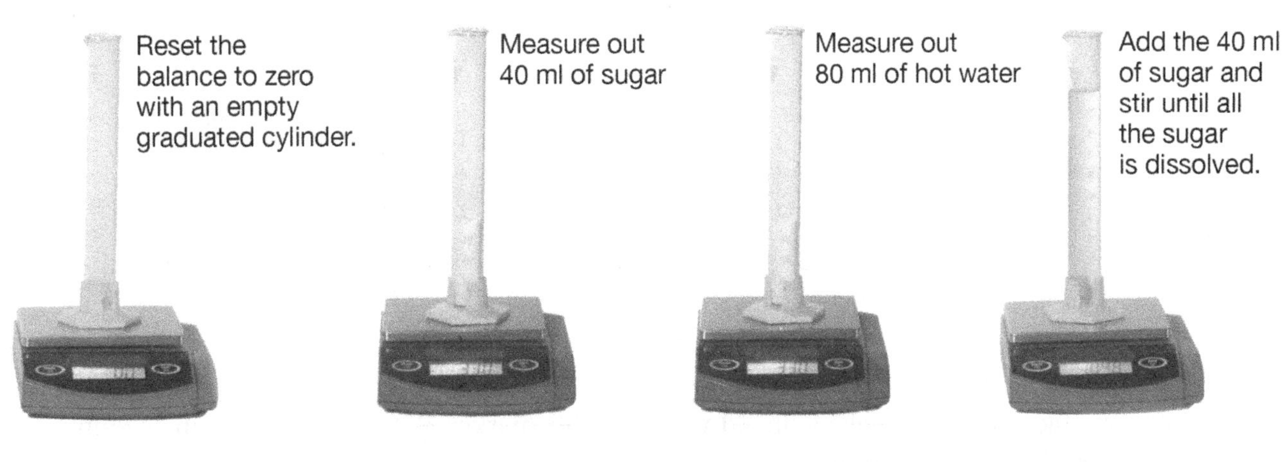

1. Put a clean, dry graduated cylinder on the balance and reset it to zero.
2. Put 40 ml of sugar into the graduated cylinder. Record the mass and volume of the sugar in Table 1 (you zeroed out the cylinder in step 1 by hitting reset on the balance while the graduated cylinder was on there, so the mass displayed by the balance will just be the sugar). Pour the sugar into a foam cup.
3. Pour 80 ml of hot water into the graduated cylinder and measure the mass.
4. Remove the graduated cylinder from the balance. Pour the 40 mL of sugar from the foam cup into the graduated cylinder containing the 80 mL of hot water and stir to dissolve all the sugar. Put the graduated cylinder back on the balance and record the mass and volume of the solution.
5. Use your mass and volume data to calculate the density of the sugar, the water, and the sugar and water solution.

Table 1: Mass and volume data for solutions

Substance	Mass in grams	Volume in mL	Density in g/mL
Sugar		40	
Water		80	
Solution of sugar and water			

2 Stop and think

a. As the sugar dissolved, you couldn't see it any more. How do you know it is all still there?

b. Compare your calculated density of sugar with your calculated density of water. Do your calculations match up with your observations? Hint; Think about density and buoyancy.

c. What happened to the volume of the water and sugar solution compared to the volume of water and sugar you started with? Can you explain this?

d. Based on the volume of water displaced by the sugar, calculate the actual density of sugar? Does this new density match up with your observations?

3 Temperature and dissolving rate

For this part of the investigation, you are going to see how sugar cubes dissolve in water of different temperatures.

1. Color one face of a sugar cube with red water-soluble marker. Put the sugar cube in an empty 100 ml beaker with the colored side facing up.
2. Color one face of a second sugar cube with blue water-soluble marker. Put the sugar cube in an empty 100 ml beaker with the colored side facing up.
3. Start the timer and carefully pour the hot or cold water down the edge of each beaker until it covers the sugar cube by about one centimeter. Do not pour the water directly on the sugar cubes!
4. Watch the colored face of each sugar cube. Which one dissolves fastest?

4 Stop and think

a. Temperature is a measure of how fast the molecules of a substance are moving. Are water molecules moving faster in hot water or cold water?

b. When a substance dissolves, molecules of the liquid crash into the solid molecules and knock some of the solid molecules loose. Explain how this concept fits with the data you observed on the dissolving sugar cubes.

16B Acids, Bases, and pH

What is pH and what does pH tell you?

pH is a number that shows whether a solution is an acid, a base, or neutral. Acids are solutions that have a pH less than 7. Bases (or alkalis) are solutions that have a pH greater than 7. A pH of 7 is called a neutral solution. pH is important because most living things can only survive in a narrow range of pH. For example, if the pH of the water in an aquarium becomes too low (acidic) or too high (alkali), the fish in the aquarium cannot survive. As you work, you will find the pH of several common solutions you probably encounter all the time. You will also learn some of the properties of acids and bases.

Materials

- Spot plates
- Pipettes
- Red cabbage juice
- Red and blue litmus paper
- 11 solutions (Table 1)
- White paper
- Safety goggles

Safety tip: Wear goggles during this investigation

1 Make a pH scale using indicators

Safety Tip: Wear goggles and a lab apron as you work. They will protect your eyes and clothing from the household chemicals that you will use.

Step 1: Prepare your sample solutions

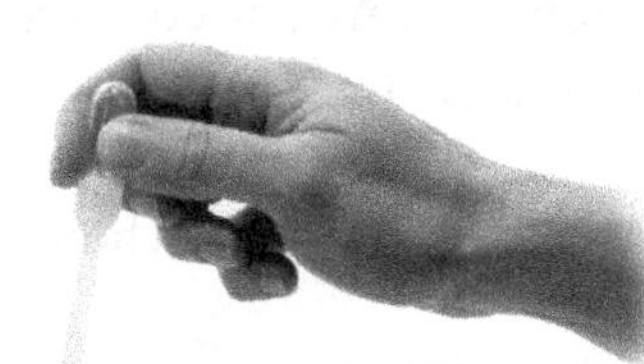

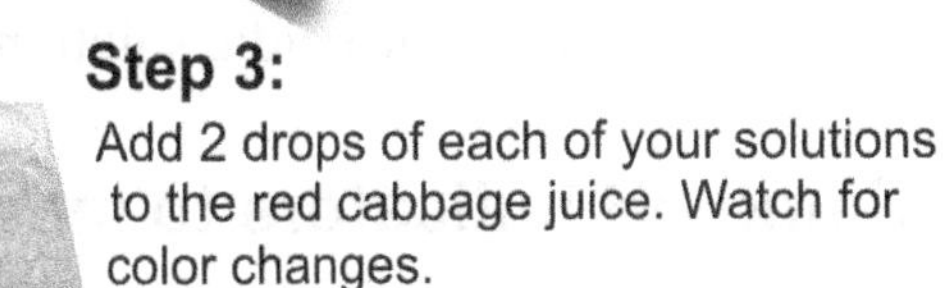

Step 3:
Add 2 drops of each of your solutions to the red cabbage juice. Watch for color changes.

Step 2:
Put 3 drops of red cabbage juice in each of 7 different wells

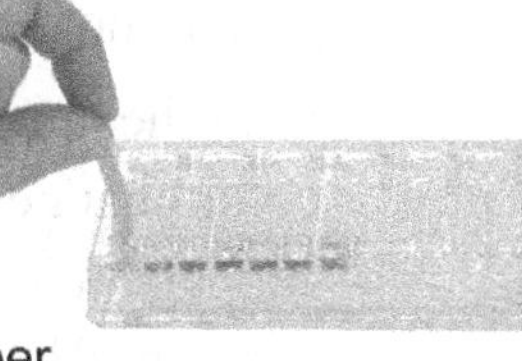

Step 4:
Dip red and blue litmus paper into each well. Observe any color changes in the litmus paper.

1. You will use the first six solutions listed in the table to create your pH color scale, but first you should prepare your work area. Place a piece of blank paper under the spot plate and mark on the paper the name of the solution and pH for each well location.
2. Use a pipette to put three drops of red cabbage juice in each of the six labeled wells.
3. Next, add two drops of each solution to the corresponding well. Use a different pipette for each solution or clean thoroughly in between each use. Write down the color changes that you see when you add the two drops of each solution. The series of color that you see on the spot plate represents a pH scale.

4. Dip the red litmus paper and the blue litmus paper into each well of the pH test plate. Use the data table to record what you see.

Table 1: Test solutions

Name of solution	Color when mixed with red cabbage juice	Red litmus paper: If paper turns blue, write "base," if no change, write "x"	Blue litmus paper: If paper turns red, write "acid," if no change, write "x"	pH
1. lemon				**2**
2. vinegar				**3**
3. seltzer				**4**
4. baking soda solution				**8.5**
5. bar soap solution				**10**
6. ammonia				**11**
7. green tea				
8. antibacterial cleaner				
9. apple juice				
10. mystery solution A				
11. mystery solution B				

2 Evaluating the role of the pH test plate

a. What is the role of a pH indicator? You used three different indicators (red cabbage juice, red litmus paper, blue litmus paper). What is the range of pH measured by each of them?

b. What general color do basic solutions turn when added to red cabbage juice?

c. What general color do acidic solutions turn when added to red cabbage juice?

3 Using pH indicators to measure unknown pH

1. Get a clean spot plate and repeat the experiment (steps 1-4) for the solutions number 7, 8, and 9. You cannot write their pH numbers because you do not know them yet.
2. Find the approximate pH of your three new solutions by looking at the color changes that happened when you added two drops of each to the red cabbage juice. Compare these color changes with your previous test plate (known pH). Also, note the litmus paper results for each solution.

How can you find the pH of these solutions?

4 Identifying mystery solutions

a. Mystery solutions A and B are the same as two other solutions that you used in this investigation. Do the pH testing with the red cabbage juice and litmus paper to identify these solutions.

b. What is the name of mystery solution A? What is the name of mystery solution B? Give evidence to support your answers.

17A Chemical Reactions

How do you know when a chemical reaction has occurred?

Chemical changes take place all around you and even inside your body. One way to tell if a chemical change has taken place is to carefully observe substances around you. When two substances combine in a chemical reaction, they form a new product that may have very different properties than the original substances. As you work, you will carefully observe some chemical reactions. Make a list of any proof that you see of chemical changes.

Materials

- Sealable plastic freezer bags
- Digital scale
- Epsom salts
- Water
- Ammonia
- Phenol red

- Raw potato
- Hydrogen peroxide
- Baking soda
- Vinegar
- Calcium chloride
- Glow stick
- Heat pack

Safety tip: Always wear goggles and an apron while you work with chemical reactions.

WARNING — This lab contains chemicals that may be harmful if misused. Read cautions on individual containers carefully. Not to be used by children except under adult supervision.

- Your teacher will give you everything you need to do each chemical reaction.
- You will do six different chemical reactions.
- Carefully follow all of the directions below.
- For each reaction, write down exactly what you see, hear, or feel. Do not use your sense of touch (except when your hands are on the outside of the baggie) and do not use your sense of taste (of course!).
- Watch for color changes, temperature changes, bubbles, new substances being formed, and production of light.
- Follow your teacher's instructions for disposal of your products when you are done.

1 Reaction #1

1. Put 5 grams of epsom salts into a baggie.
2. Add 10 milliliters of ammonia solution to the baggie. Close it tightly.
3. Feel the baggie with your hands as the reaction is taking place.
4. Let the baggie sit until you are done with all six reactions. Then look at this baggie again.

2 Reaction #2

1. Place a potato slice into a baggie.
2. Add 10 milliliters of hydrogen peroxide to the baggie. Close it tightly.
3. Feel the baggie with your hands as the reaction is taking place. You can even hold it up to your ear and listen to the reaction.
4. Let the baggie sit until you are done with all six reactions. Then look at this baggie again.

3 Reaction #3

1. Put 5 grams of baking soda into a baggie.
2. Add 10 milliliters of phenol red and 10 milliliters of vinegar to the baggie. Close it tightly.
3. Feel the baggie with your hands as the reaction is taking place.
4. Let the baggie sit until you are done with all six reactions. Then look at this baggie again.

4 Reaction #4

1. Put 10 grams of calcium chloride into a baggie. Then put 5 grams of baking soda in with it.
2. Add 10 milliliters of phenol red to the baggie. Quickly close it tightly.
3. Feel the baggie with your hands as the reaction is taking place.
4. Let the baggie sit until you are done with all six reactions. Then look at this baggie again.

5 Reaction #5

1. Activate a glow stick as instructed by your teacher.
2. Watch and feel the glow stick as the reaction is taking place.

6 Reaction #6

1. Activate a heat pack as instructed by your teacher.
2. Feel the heat pack with your hands as the reaction is taking place.

7 Stop and think

a. Organize your observations in the data table below. For each observation category, list the reactions that match those observations. The first row has been completed for you.

observation category	reaction number
color change	Reactions 3 and 4 showed a color change.
temperature change	
bubbles/gas formation	
precipitate	
light emission	

b. Reaction 2 uses hydrogen peroxide and a slice of potato. You may have used hydrogen peroxide before to clean out a wound in your skin. Whenever hydrogen peroxide comes into contact with damaged cells, like a potato cut or a skin cut, it bubbles and foams. How might this help clean out a skin wound?

c. Calcium chloride is used in reaction 4. Do some Internet research to find common uses for calcium chloride. How does this make sense, based on your observations of reaction 4?

17B Conservation of Mass

How do scientists describe what happens in a chemical reaction?

A French chemist named Antoine Lavoisier was the first to prove the law of conservation of mass. This law says that the total mass of the reactants in a chemical reaction is always equal to the total mass of the products. This is not as easy to see as you might think! As you do this investigation, you will discover how tricky it is to show the law of conservation of mass.

Materials

- Periodic Table Tiles
- Effervescent tablet
- Digital scale
- Water
- Small paper cup

Safety tip: Wear goggles and an apron as you work

WARNING — This lab contains chemicals that may be harmful if misused. Read cautions on individual containers carefully. Not to be used by children except under adult supervision.

1 Testing the reaction

Step 1:
Tare the balance to zero with the empty cup

Step 2:
Measure the mass of water and tablet

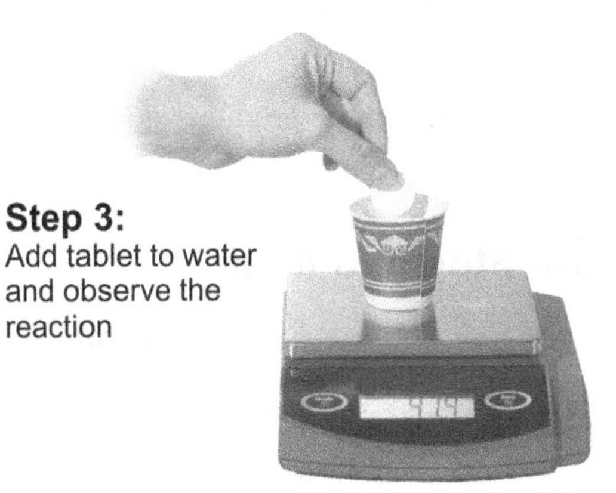

Step 3:
Add tablet to water and observe the reaction

Table 1: Conservation of mass data

Step	Data and observations
1. Find the mass of the effervescent tablet.	
2. Put the paper cup on the balance and tare it to zero. Fill the cup about halfway with water. Record the mass.	
3. Put the tablet on the balance beside the cup, but don't put it in the water yet. Record the total starting mass.	
4. Drop the tablet into the cup of water. You can do this while the cup is still on the balance. Record your observations.	
5. Wait for the reaction to stop. Then, tap the cup gently to release as many bubbles as you can. Measure the mass.	
6. Subtract the final mass (5) from the starting mass (3). This is the mass difference between the products and reactants.	

2 Stop and think

a. Does this experiment agree with the law of conservation of mass? Look at the data that you just recorded. Use it to help you to explain why or why not.

b. Explain why you observed a difference in mass. Where did the missing mass go? Did it really disappear?

3 Modeling the reaction

Scientists write chemical reactions like mathematical formulas. The reactants are to the left of the arrow and the products are to the right of the arrow.

Reactants → Products

Use the tiles to model the chemical reaction

The effervescent tablet contains a chemical called sodium bicarbonate. This chemical reacts with water according to the following reaction.

$$H_2O + NaHCO_3 \rightarrow NaOH + CO_2 + H_2O$$

1. Build the reactants side ($H_2O + NaHCO_3$) of the chemical reaction above using the periodic table tiles.
2. Build the products side ($NaOH + CO_2 + H_2O$) of the chemical reaction using more periodic table tiles.

4 Stop and think

Table 2: Counting atoms of each element

Element	Reactants	Products
Hydrogen		
Carbon		
Oxygen		
Sodium		

a. Fill in Table 2 with the numbers of each type of atom on the reactant side of the equation and on the product side of the equation.

b. How do the numbers of atoms of each element compare on the reactant and product side of the equation? What does this imply for the law of conservation of mass?

c. In what phase are each of the reactants (solid, liquid, or gas)? In what phase are each of the three products (solid, liquid, or gas)?

d. Suggest a way to do the experiment that could better demonstrate conservation of mass.

18A Carbon and its Chemistry

What are some common molecules that contain carbon?

Living organisms are made up of a great variety of molecules, but the number of different elements involved is very small. Organic chemistry is the science of molecules that contain carbon and these are the ones most important to living organisms. This investigation will introduce you to some small organic molecules.

Materials

- Periodic Table Tiles
- Reference book of organic compounds

1 The chemistry of carbon

Carbon is the central element in the chemistry of living things. This is because carbon can make complex molecules. Each carbon atom can make four bonds because carbon has four electrons in the outer energy level, which can hold a total of eight. Carbon can also form double and triple bonds by sharing two or three electrons with a single atom. Because of carbon's flexible bonding ability, many molecular structures are possible.

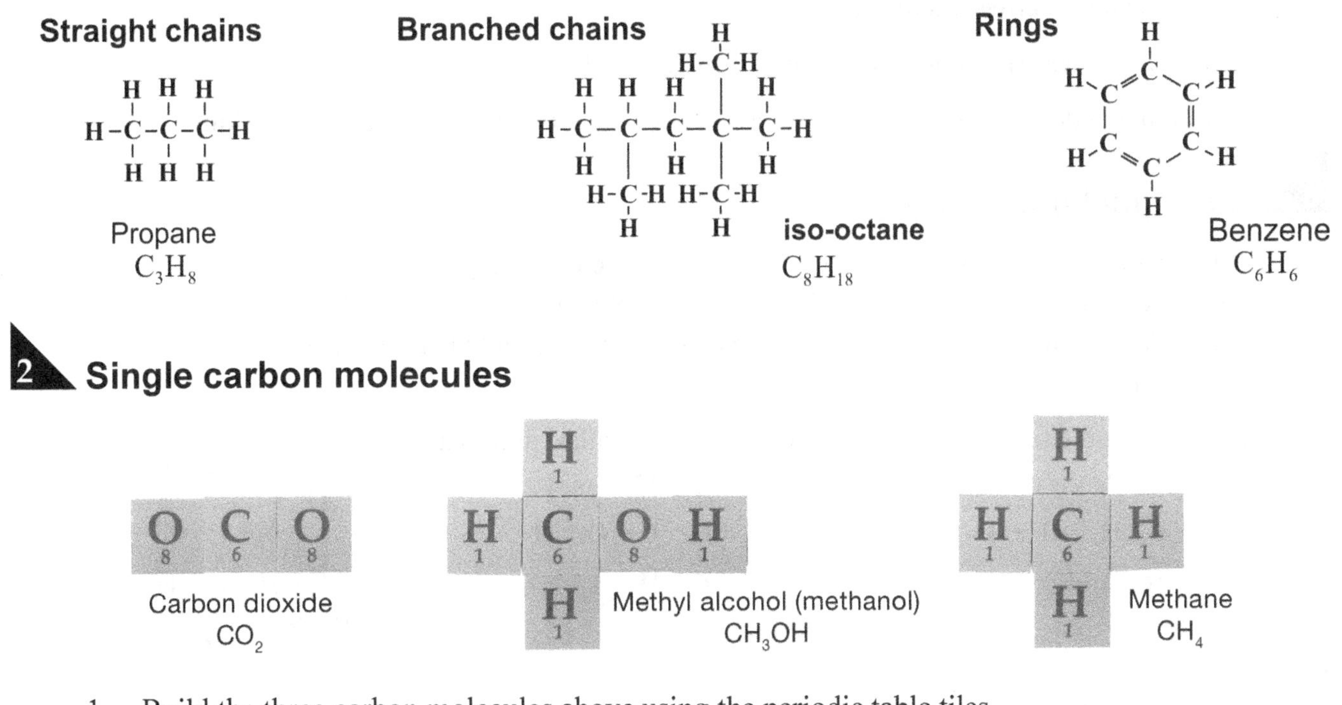

2 Single carbon molecules

1. Build the three carbon molecules above using the periodic table tiles.
2. Build a model of carbonic acid: H_2CO_3.

3 Stop and think

a. Research and describe three reactions which use or produce carbon dioxide.

b. Research and describe at least one use of methyl alcohol.

c. Research and describe the use and production of methane.

4 Molecules with two carbon atoms

Once there are two carbon atoms, the structures get more complicated. The carbon atoms may share a single, double, or triple bond between them.

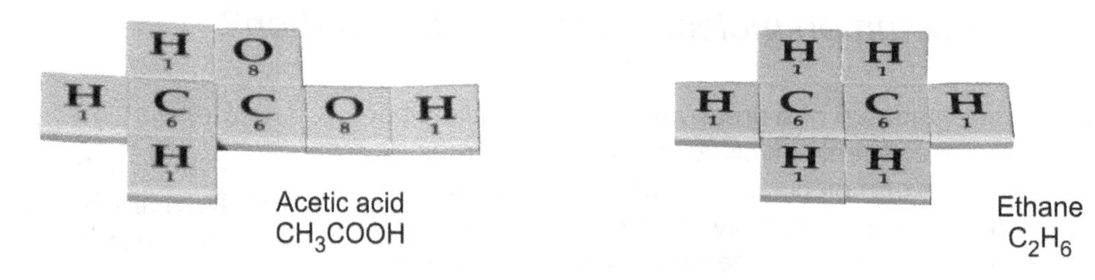

1. Build the 2-carbon molecules above using the periodic table tiles.
2. Build a model of ethyl alcohol (ethanol): C_2H_5OH.
   (Hint: Each carbon atom makes 4 bonds and the oxygen atom makes two bonds)
3. Build a model of acetylene: C_2H_2.
   (Hint: there is a triple bond between the two carbon atoms)

5 Stop and think

a. Research and describe where acetic acid is found.

b. Research and describe at least one use of ethyl alcohol.

c. Research and describe a reaction between acetylene and oxygen that is used in welding metal.

6 Biological molecules

Living organisms are constructed mainly of proteins, which are very large carbon-based molecules, such as hemoglobin (right). A single protein may contain 10,000 or more atoms. Proteins themselves are constructed of simpler units called amino acids. For example, the hemoglobin molecule contains 584 amino acids.

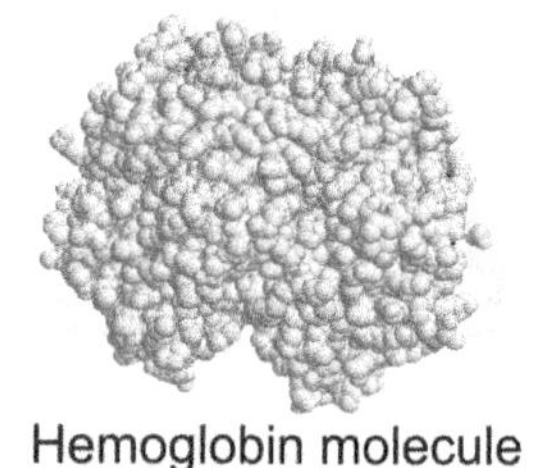
Hemoglobin molecule

Use the periodic table tiles to build models of the three smallest amino acids.

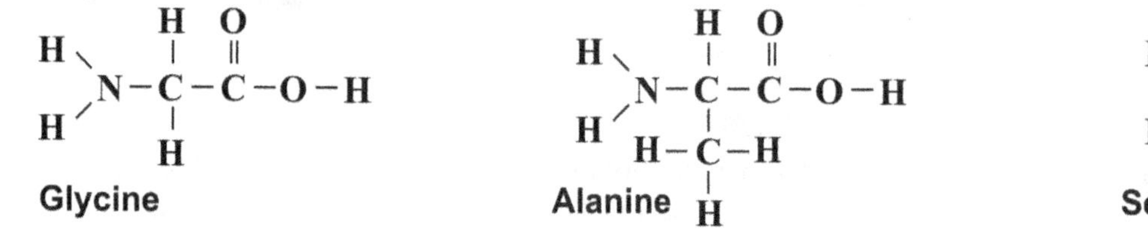

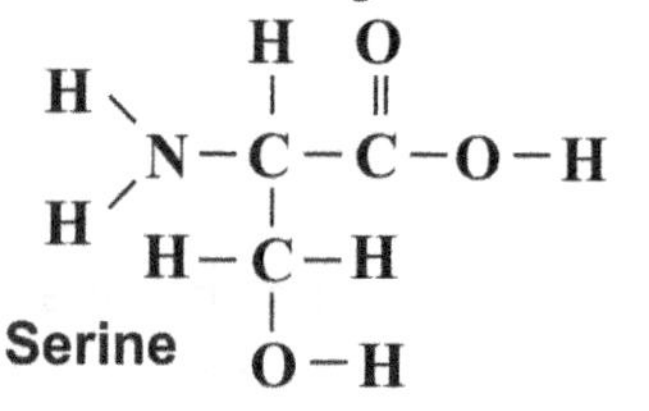

7 Stop and think

a. What is similar about all three amino acids?

b. Is the chemical in the diagram on the right an amino acid? Explain why you think your answer is correct.

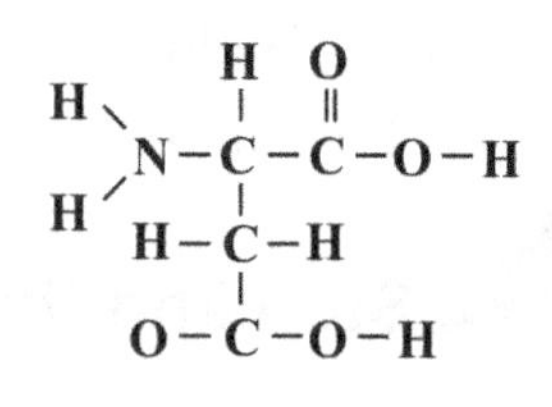
Is this an amino acid?

18B The Structure of DNA

How does a DNA molecule carry information?

DNA is found in all living creatures we know. This complex molecule contains the information on how to build every protein used in your body. DNA is like a blueprint for building a living creature. The DNA molecule itself is a fascinating structure, as you will see in this activity.

Materials

- Licorice sticks (about 6" long)
- Round toothpicks
- Colored gumdrops

1 About the DNA molecule

A DNA molecule is put together like a twisted ladder, or double helix. Each side of each rung of the ladder is made of a 5-carbon sugar called deoxyribose, a phosphate group, and a nitrogen base. Two nitrogen bases are paired in the center of the ladder so each rung is composed of two similar groups.

The genetic code in a DNA molecule is stored in the sequence of the nitrogen bases. For example the sequence AATGCA is coded in the DNA molecule in the diagram.

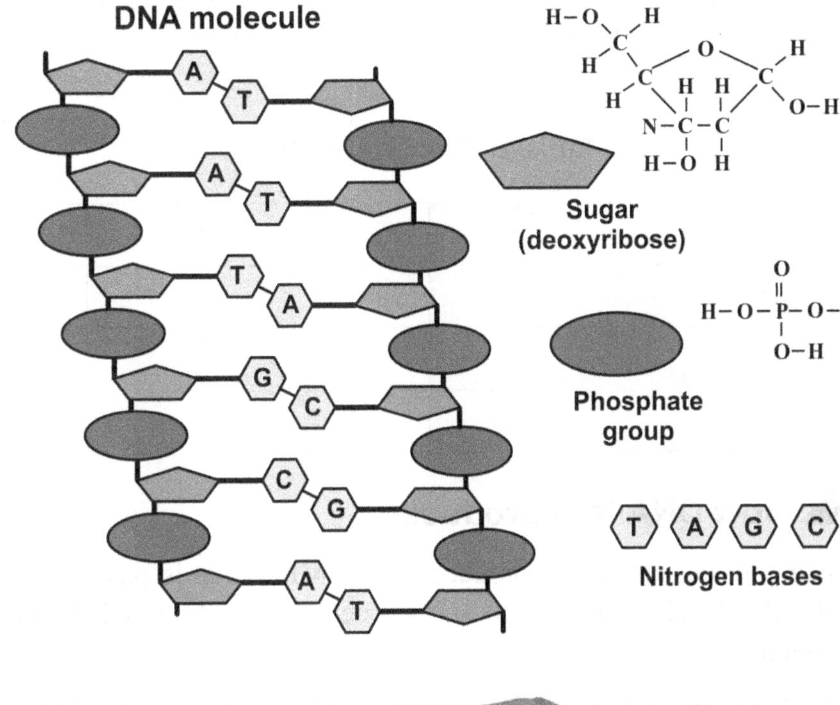

2 Building a DNA molecule out of gum drops

There are four different nitrogen base groups in a DNA molecule. Each should be represented with a different colored gumdrop. Choose the color you want to use to represent each nitrogen base (A, G, C, T).

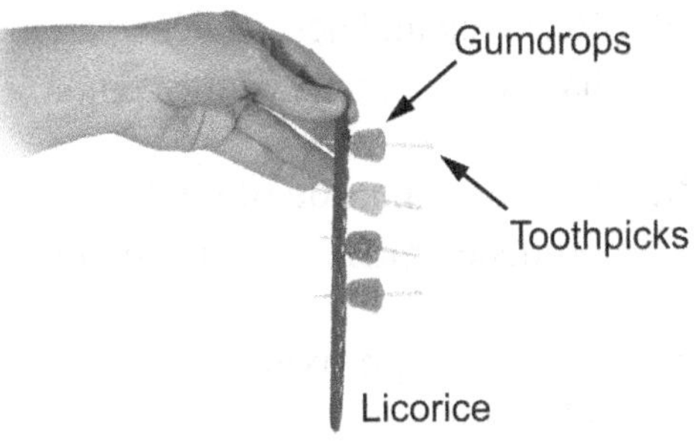

Table 1: Nitrogen base colors

Adenine (A)	Guanine (G)	Cytosine (C)	Thymine (T)

1. The licorice will be the backbone of sugar and phosphate. Put 8 toothpicks through the licorice (evenly spaced) and push a gumdrop past the middle of each toothpick.
2. The color sequence of your gumdrops will be your DNA code!

3 Pairing up the nitrogen bases

The nitrogen bases in a DNA molecule pair up with each other. Adenine pairs with thymine and guanine pairs with cytosine.

1. Use Table 2 to record the 8-letter genetic code for the left side of your DNA molecule. Put the colors in row 1 and the letter codes in row 2.
2. Use the pairing of the nitrogen bases (A-T or C-G) to complete row 3 for the right side of your DNA molecule.
3. Use Table 1 to determine which gumdrop colors correspond to the nitrogen bases in row 3.
4. Complete your DNA molecule by building the opposite half of the ladder! You can give your DNA ladder a gentle twist so it looks like the real double helix shape.

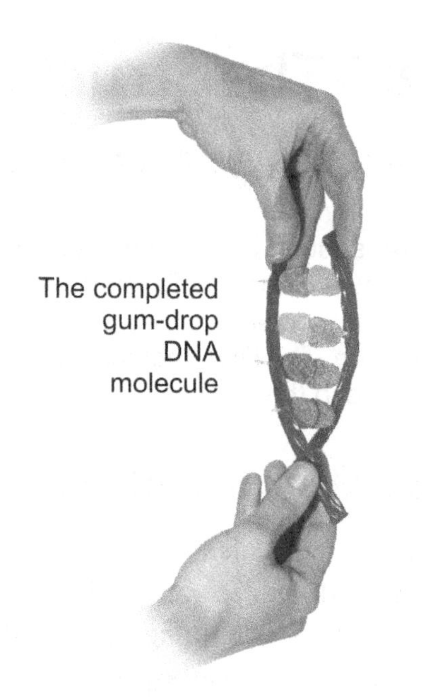
The completed gum-drop DNA molecule

Table 2: The DNA code

1	Colors								
2	Letters (A, G, C, T)								
3	Letters (A, G, C, T)								
4	Colors								

4 How DNA is reproduced

When a living creature reproduces, its genetic code is passed on to its offspring through DNA. On the molecular level, reproduction starts when the DNA strand divides down the center, splitting apart the nitrogen bases.

a. Research and describe how an identical new DNA molecule is created once the original DNA molecule has been split down the center.

b. Suppose one side of a DNA molecule had the nitrogen base sequence TAGGCCA. What nitrogen base sequence must be on the other side of the DNA molecule?

c. Research approximately how many base pairs are in a typical DNA molecule such as might be found in a human cell.

Lab Skills and Equipment Setups

Safety Skills

What can I do to protect myself and others in the lab?

Science equipment and supplies are fun to use. However, these materials must always be used with care. Here you will learn how to be safe in a science lab.

Materials

- Poster board
- Felt-tip markers

1 Follow these basic safety guidelines

Your teacher will divide the class into groups. Each group should create a poster-sized display of one of the following guidelines. Hang the posters in the lab. Review these safety guidelines before each Investigation.

1. **Prepare** for each Investigation.
   a. Read the Investigation sheets carefully.
   b. Take special note of safety instructions.
2. **Listen** to your teacher's instructions before, during, and after the Investigation. Take notes to help you remember what your teacher has said.
3. **Get ready to work:** Roll long sleeves above the wrist. Tie back long hair. Remove dangling jewelry and any loose, bulky outer layers of clothing. Wear shoes that cover the toes.
4. **Gather** protective clothing (goggles, apron, gloves) at the beginning of the Investigation.
5. **Emphasize teamwork**. Help each other. Watch out for one another's safety.
6. **Clean up** spills immediately. Clean up all materials and supplies after an Investigation.

2 Know what to do when...

1. **working with heat.**
   a. Always handle hot items with a hot pad. Never use your bare hands.
   b. Move carefully when you are near hot items. Sudden movements could cause burns if you touch or spill something hot.
   c. Inform others if they are near hot items or liquids
2. **working with electricity.**
   a. Always keep electric cords away from water.
   b. Extension cords must not be placed where they may cause someone to trip or fall.
   c. If an electrical appliance isn't working, feels hot, or smells hot, tell a teacher right away.

3. **disposing of materials and supplies.**

   a. Generally, liquid household chemicals can be poured into a sink. Completely wash the chemical down the drain with plenty of water.

   b. Generally, solid household chemicals can be placed in a trash can.

   c. Any liquids or solids that **should not** be poured down the sink or placed in the trash have special disposal guidelines. Follow your teacher's instructions.

   d. If glass breaks, do not use your bare hands to pick up the pieces. Use a dustpan and a brush to clean up. "Sharps" trash (trash that has pieces of glass) should be well labeled. The best way to throw away broken glass is to seal it in a labeled cardboard box.

4. **you are concerned about your safety or the safety of others.**

   a. Talk to your teacher immediately. Here are some examples:

      - You smell chemical or gas fumes. This might indicate a chemical or gas leak.
      - You smell something burning.
      - You injure yourself or see someone else who is injured.
      - You are having trouble using your equipment.
      - You do not understand the instructions for the Investigation.

   b. Listen carefully to your teacher's instructions.

   c. Follow your teacher's instructions exactly.

3 Safety quiz

1. Draw a diagram of your science lab in the space below. Include in your diagram the following items. Include notes that explain how to use these important safety items.

- Exit/entrance ways
- Fire extinguisher(s)
- Fire blanket
- Eye wash and shower
- First aid kit
- Location of eye goggles and lab aprons
- Sink
- Trash cans
- Location of special safety instructions

2. How many fire extinguishers are in your science lab? Explain how to use them.

3. List the steps that your teacher and your class would take to safely exit the science lab and the building in case of a fire or other emergency.

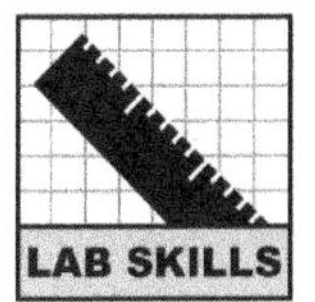

4. Before beginning certain Investigations, why should you first put on protective goggles and clothing?

5. Why is teamwork important when you are working in a science lab?

6. Why should you clean up after every Investigation?

7. List at least three things you should you do if you sense danger or see an emergency in your classroom or lab.

8. Five lab situations are described below. What would you do in each situation?
   a. You accidentally knock over a glass container and it breaks on the floor.

   b. You accidentally spill a large amount of water on the floor.

c. You suddenly you begin to smell a “chemical” odor that gives you a headache.

d. You hear the fire alarm while you are working in the lab. You are wearing your goggles and lab apron.

e. While your lab partner has her lab goggles off, she gets some liquid from the experiment in her eye.

f. A fire starts in the lab.

Safety in the science lab is everyone’s responsibility!

4 Safety contract

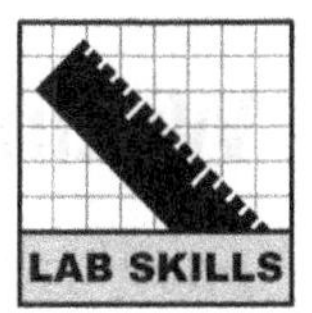

Keep this contract in your notebook at all times.

By signing it, you agree to follow all the steps necessary to be safe in your science class and lab.

I, ____________________, (Your name)

- Have learned about the use and location of the following:
  - Aprons, gloves
  - Eye protection
  - Eyewash fountain
  - Fire extinguisher and fire blanket
  - First aid kit
  - Heat sources (burners, hot plate, etc) and how to use them safely
  - Waste-disposal containers for glass, chemicals, matches, paper, and wood
- Understand the safety information presented.
- Will ask questions when I do not understand safety instructions.
- Pledge to follow all of the safety guidelines that are presented on the Safety Skill Sheet at all times.
- Pledge to follow all of the safety guidelines that are presented on Investigation sheets.
- Will always follow the safety instructions that my teacher provides.

Additionally, I pledge to be careful about my own safety and to help others be safe. I understand that I am responsible for helping to create a safe environment in the classroom and lab.

Signed and dated,

____

Parent's or Guardian's statement:

I have read the Safety Skills sheet and give my consent for the student who has signed the preceding statement to engage in laboratory activities using a variety of equipment and materials, including those described. I pledge my cooperation in urging that she or he observe the safety regulations prescribed.

____ ______________________________

Signature of Parent or Guardian Date

Writing a Lab Report

How do you share the results of an experiment?

A lab report is like a story about an experiment. The details in the story help others learn from what you did. A good lab report makes it possible for someone else to repeat your experiment. If their results and conclusions are similar to yours, you have support for your ideas. Through this process we come to understand more about how the world works.

1 The parts of a lab report

A lab report follows the steps of the scientific method. Use the checklist below to create your own lab reports:

- ☐ **Title:** The title makes it easy for readers to quickly identify the topic of your experiment.
- ☐ **Research question:** The research question tells the reader exactly what you want to find out through your experiment.
- ☐ **Introduction:** This paragraph describes what you already know about the topic, and shows how this information relates to your experiment.
- ☐ **Hypothesis:** The hypothesis states the prediction you plan to test in your experiment.
- ☐ **Materials:** List all the materials you need to do the experiment.
- ☐ **Procedure:** Describe the steps involved in your experiment. Make sure that you provide enough detail so readers can repeat what you did. You may want to provide sketches of the lab setup. Be sure to name the experimental variable and tell which variables you controlled.
- ☐ **Data/Observations:** This is where you record what happened, using descriptive words, data tables, and graphs.
- ☐ **Analysis:** In this section, describe your data in words. Here's a good way to start: *My data shows that...*
- ☐ **Conclusion:** This paragraph states whether your hypothesis was correct or incorrect. It may suggest a new research question or a new hypothesis.

2 A sample lab report

Use the sample lab report on the next two pages as a guide for writing your own lab reports. Remember that you are telling a story about something you did so that others can repeat your experiment.

Name: Lucy O. **Date:** January 24, 2007

Title: Pressure and Speed

Research question: How does pressure affect the speed of the CPO air rocket?

Introduction:

Air pressure is a term used to describe how tightly air molecules are packed into a certain space. When air pressure increases, more air molecules are packed into the same amount of space. These molecules are moving around and colliding with each other and the walls of the container. As the number of molecules in the container increases, the number of molecular collisions in the container increases. A pressure gauge measures the force of these molecules as they strike a surface.

In this lab, I will measure the speed of the CPO air rocket when it is launched with different amounts of initial pressure inside the plastic bottle. I want to know if a greater amount of initial air pressure will cause the air rocket to travel at a greater speed.

Hypothesis: When I increase the pressure of the air rocket, the speed will increase.

Materials:

CPO air rocket

CPO photogates

CPO timer

Goggles

Procedure:

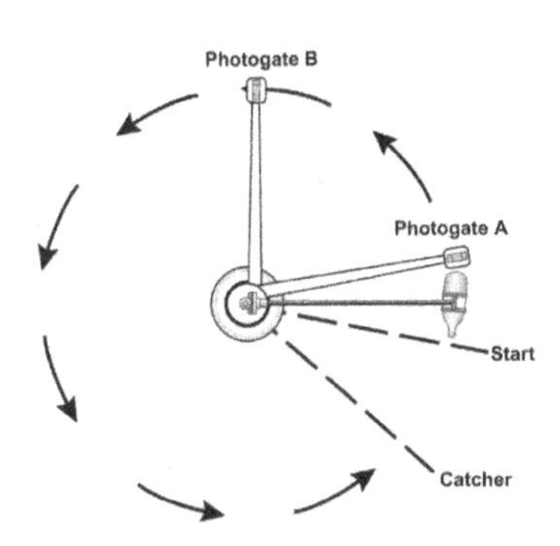

1. I put on goggles and made sure the area was clear.
2. The air rocket is attached to an arm so that it travels in a circular path. After it travels about 330°, the air rocket hits a stopper and its flight ends. I set up the photogate at 90°.
3. My control variables were the mass of the rocket and launch technique, so I kept these constant throughout the experiment.
4. My experimental variable was the initial pressure applied to the rocket. I tested the air rocket at three different initial pressures. The pressures that work effectively with this equipment range from 15 psi to 90 psi. I tested the air rocket at 20 psi, 50 psi, and 80 psi. I did three trials at each pressure.
5. The length of the rocket wing is 5 cm. The wing breaks the photogate's light beam. The photogate reports the amount of time that the wing took to pass through the beam. Therefore, I used wing length as distance and divide by time to calculate speed of the air rocket.
6. I found the average speed in centimeters per second for each pressure.

Data/Observations:

Table 1: Air pressure and speed of rocket

Initial air pressure	Time (sec) at 90°	Speed (m/sec) at 90°	Average speed cm/sec
20 psi	0.0227	2.20	216
	0.0231	2.16	
	0.0237	2.11	
50 psi	0.0097	5.15	510
	0.0099	5.05	
	0.0098	5.10	
80 psi	0.0060	8.33	794
	0.0064	7.81	
	0.0065	7.69	

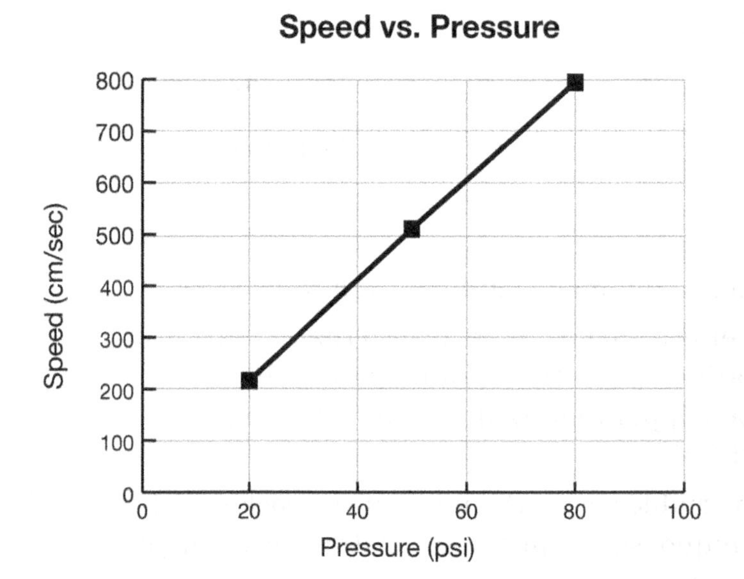

Analysis:

My graph shows that the plots of the data for photogates A and B are linear. As the values for pressure increased, the speed increased also.

Conclusion:

The data shows that pressure does have an effect on speed. The graph shows that my hypothesis is correct. As the initial pressure of the rocket increased, the speed of the rocket increased as well. There is a direct relationship between pressure and speed of the rocket.

LAB SKILLS

Measuring Length

How do you find the length of an object?

Size matters! When you describe the length of an object, or the distance between two objects, you are describing something very important about the object. Is it as small as a bacteria (2 micrometers)? Is it a light year away (9.46 × 10^{15} meters)? By using the metric system you can quickly see the difference in size between objects.

Materials

- Metric ruler
- Pencil
- Paper
- Small objects
- Calculator

1 Reading the meter scale correctly

Look at the ruler in the picture above. Each small line on the top of the ruler represents one millimeter. Larger lines stand for 5 millimeter and 10 millimeter intervals. When the object you are measuring falls between the lines, read the number to the nearest 0.5 millimeter. Practice measuring several objects with your own metric ruler. Compare your results with a lab partner.

2 Stop and think

a. You may have seen a ruler like this marked in centimeter units. How many millimeters are in one centimeter?

____

____

____

b. Notice that the ruler also has markings for reading the English system. Give an example of when it would be better to measure with the English system than the metric system. Give a different example of when it would be better to use the metric system.

____

____

____

3 Example 1: Measuring objects correctly

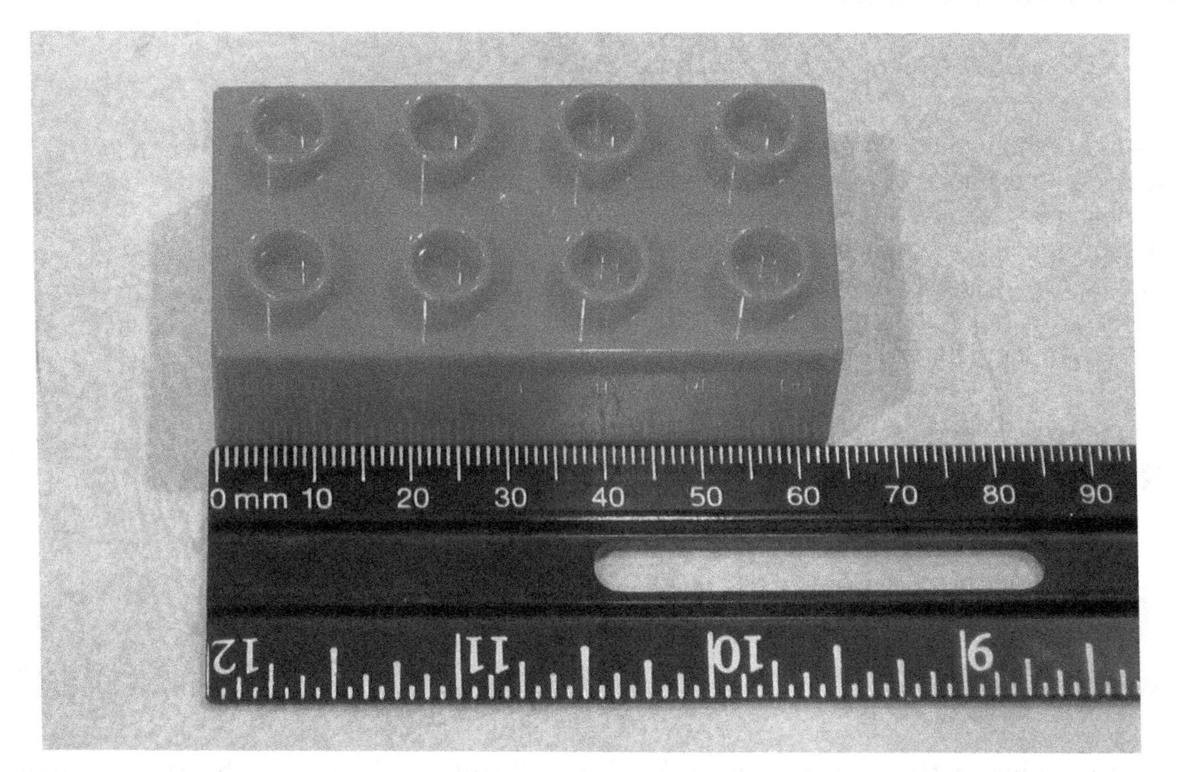

Look at the picture above. How long is the building block?

1. Report the length of the building block to the nearest 0.5 millimeters.
2. Convert your answer to centimeters.
3. Convert your answer to meters.

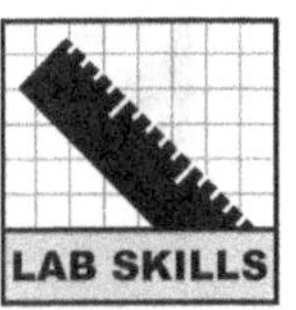

4 Example 2: Measuring objects correctly

Look at the picture above. How long is the pencil?

1. Report the length of the pencil to the nearest 0.5 millimeters.
2. Challenge: How many building blocks in example 1 will it take to equal the length of the pencil?
3. Challenge: Convert the length of the pencil to inches by dividing your answer by 25.4 millimeters per inch.

5 Example 3: Measuring objects correctly

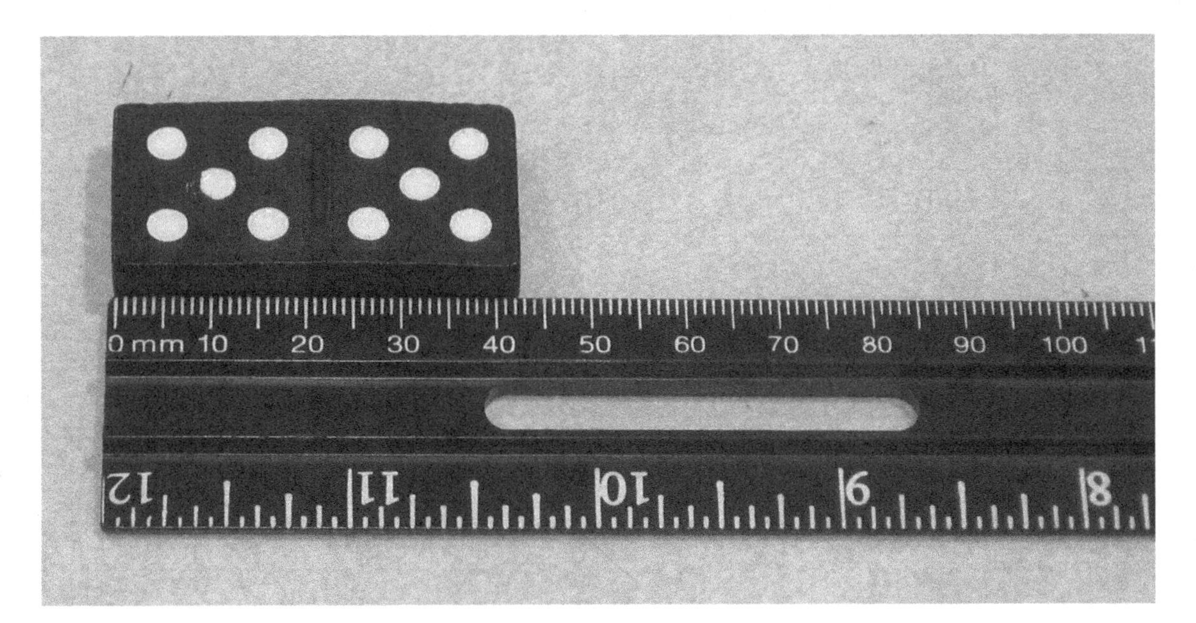

Look at the picture above. How long is the domino?

1. Report the length of the domino to the nearest 0.5 millimeters.
2. Challenge: How many dominoes will fit end to end on the 30 cm ruler?

6 Practice converting units for length

By completing the examples above you show that you are familiar with some of the prefixes used in the metric system like milli- and centi-. The table below gives other prefixes you may be less familiar with. Try converting the length of the domino from millimeters into all the other units given in the table.

Refer to the multiplication factor this way:

- 1 kilometer equals 1000 meters.
- 1000 millimeters equals 1 meter.

1. How many millimeters are in a kilometer?

1000 millimeters per meter × 1000 meters per kilometer = 1,000,000 millimeters per kilometer

2. Fill in the table with your multiplication factor by converting millimeters to the unit given. The first one is done for you.

1000 millimeters per meter × 10^{-12} meters per picometer = 10^{-9} millimeters per picometer

3. Divide the domino's length in millimeters by the number in your multiplication factor column. This is the answer you will put in the last column.

Prefix	Symbol	Multiplication factor	Scientific notation in meters	Your multiplication factor	Your domino length in:
pico-	p	0.000000000001	10^{-12}	10^{-9}	pm
nano-	n	0.000000001	10^{-9}		nm
micro-	μ	0.000001	10^{-6}		μm
milli	m	0.001	10^{-3}		mm
centi-	c	0.01	10^{-2}		cm
deci-	d	0.1	10^{-1}		dm
deka-	da	10	10^{1}		dam
hecto-	h	100	10^{2}		hm
kilo-	k	1000	10^{3}		km

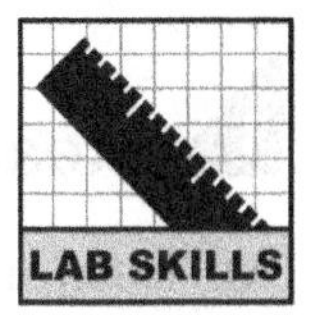

Measuring Temperature

How do you find the temperature of a substance?

There are many different kinds of thermometers used to measure temperature. Can you think of some you find at home? In your classroom you will use a glass immersion thermometer to find the temperature of a liquid. The thermometer contains alcohol with a red dye in it so you can see the alcohol level inside the thermometer. The alcohol level changes depending on the surrounding temperature. You will practice reading the scale on the thermometer and report your readings in degrees Celsius.

Materials

- Alcohol immersion thermometer
- Beakers
- Water at different temperatures
- Ice

Safety: Glass thermometers are breakable. Handle them carefully. Overheating the thermometer can cause the alcohol to separate and give incorrect readings. Glass thermometers should be stored horizontally or vertically (never upside down) to prevent alcohol from separating.

1 Reading the temperature scale correctly

Look at the picture at right. See the close-up of the line inside the thermometer on the scale. The tens scale numbers are given. The ones scale appears as lines. Each small line equals 1 degree Celsius. Practice reading the scale from the bottom to the top. One small line above 20°C is read as 21°C. When the level of the alcohol is between two small lines on the scale, report the number to the nearest 0.5°C.

2 Stop and think

a. What number does the large line between 20°C and 30°C equal? Figure out by counting the number of small lines between 20°C and 30°C.

b. Give the temperature of the thermometer in the picture above.

c. Practice rounding the following temperature values to the nearest 0.5°C: 23.1°C, 29.8°C, 30.0°C, 31.6°C, 31.4°C.

d. Water at 0°C and 100°C has different properties. Describe what water looks like at these temperatures.

e. What will happen to the level of the alcohol if you hold the thermometer by the bulb?

3 Reading the temperature of water in a beaker

An immersion thermometer must be placed in liquid up to the solid line on the thermometer (at least 2 and one half inches of liquid). Wait about 3 minutes for the temperature of the thermometer to equal the temperature of the liquid. Record the temperature to the nearest 0.5°C when the level stops moving.

1. Place the thermometer in the beaker. Check to make sure that the water level is above the solid line on the thermometer.

2. Wait until the alcohol level stops moving (about three minutes). Record the temperature to the nearest 0.5°C.

4 Reading the temperature of warm water in a beaker

A warm liquid will cool to room temperature. For a warm liquid, record the warmest temperature you observe before the temperature begins to decrease.

1. Repeat the procedure above with a beaker of warm (not boiling) water.

2. Take temperature readings every 30 seconds. Record the warmest temperature you observe.

5 Reading the temperature of ice water in a beaker

When a large amount of ice is added to water, the temperature of the water will drop until the ice and water are the same temperature. After the ice has melted, the cold water will warm to room temperature.

1. Repeat the procedure above with a beaker of ice and water.

2. Take temperature readings every 30 seconds. Record the coldest temperature you observe.

Calculating Volume

How do you find the volume of a three dimensional shape?

Volume is the amount of space an object takes up. If you know the dimensions of a solid object, you can find the object's volume. A two dimensional shape has length and width. A three dimensional object has length, width, and height. This investigation will give you practice finding volume for different solid objects.

Materials

- Pencil
- Calculator

1 Calculating volume of a cube

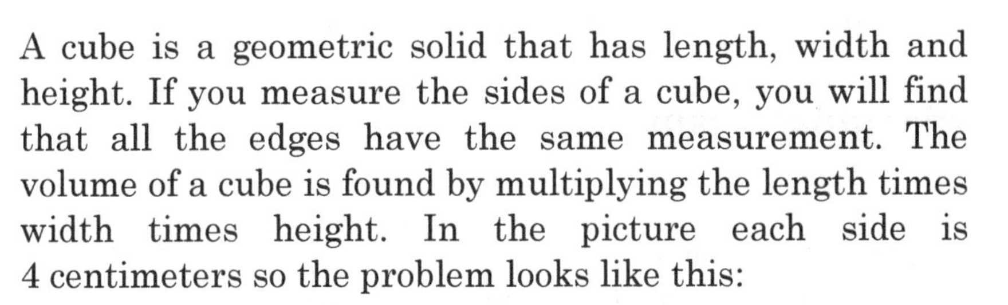

A cube is a geometric solid that has length, width and height. If you measure the sides of a cube, you will find that all the edges have the same measurement. The volume of a cube is found by multiplying the length times width times height. In the picture each side is 4 centimeters so the problem looks like this:

$$V = l \times w \times h$$

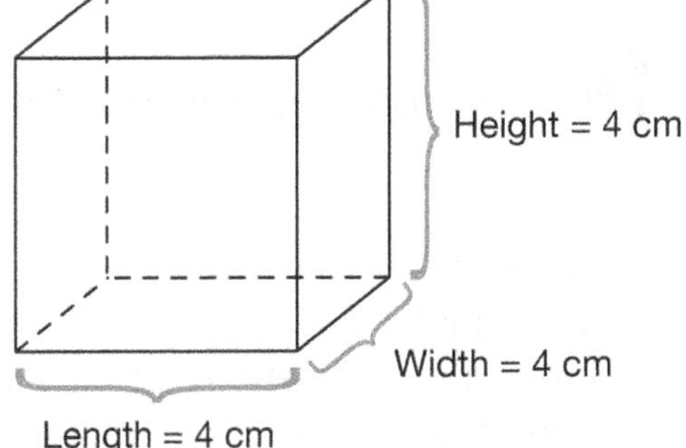

Example:

Volume = 4 centimeters × 4 centimeters × 4 centimeters = 64 centimeters^3

2 Stop and think

a. What are the units for volume in the example above?

b. In the example above, if the edge of the cube is 4 inches, what will the volume be? Give the units.

c. How is finding volume different from finding area?

d. If you had cubes with a length of 1 centimeter, how many would you need to build the cube in the picture above?

3 Calculating volume of a rectangular prism

Height = 2 cm

Width = 3 cm

Length = 8 cm

Rectangular prisms are like cubes, except not all of the sides are equal. A shoebox is a rectangular prism. You can find the volume of a rectangular prism using the same formula given above $V = l \times w \times h$.

Another way to say it is to multiply the area of the base times the height.

1. Find the area of the base for the rectangular prism pictured above.
2. Multiply the area of the base times the height. Record the volume of the rectangular prism.
3. PRACTICE: Find the volume for a rectangular prism with a height 6 cm, length 5 cm, and width 3 cm. Be sure to include the units in all of your answers.

4 Calculating volume for a triangular prism

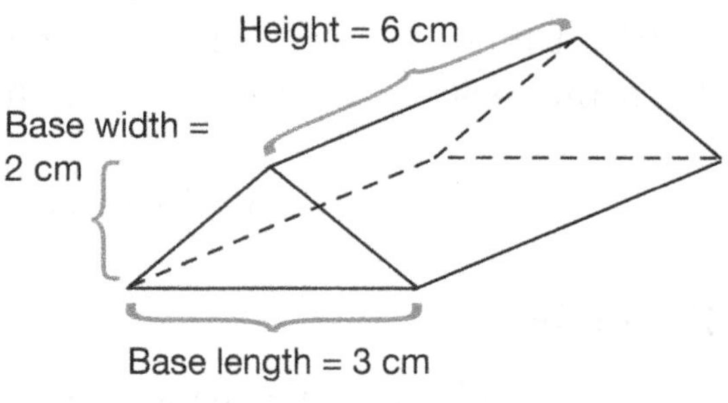

Triangular prisms have three sides and two triangular bases. The volume of the triangular prism is found by multiplying the area of the base times the height. The base is a triangle.

1. Find the area of the base by solving for the area of the triangle: $B = {}^{1}/_{2} \times l \times w$.
2. Find the volume by multiplying the area of the base times the height of the prism: $V = B \times h$. Record the volume of the triangular prism shown above.
3. PRACTICE: Find the volume of the triangular prism with a height 10 cm, triangular base width 4 cm, and triangular base length 5 cm.

5 Calculating volume for a cylinder

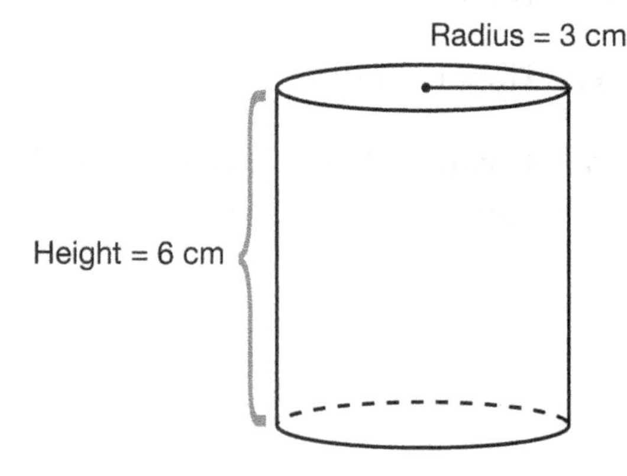

A soup can is a cylinder. A cylinder has two circular bases and a round surface. The volume of the cylinder is found by multiplying the area of the base times the height. The base is a circle.

1. Find the area of the base by solving for the area of a circle: $A = \pi \times r^2$.
2. Find the volume by multiplying the area of the base times the height of the cylinder: $V = A \times h$. Record the volume of the cylinder shown above.
3. PRACTICE: Find the volume of the cylinder with height 8 cm and radius 4 cm.

6 Calculating volume for a cone

An ice cream cone really is a cone! A cone has height and a circular base. The volume of the cone is found by multiplying $^1/_2$ times the area of the base times the height.

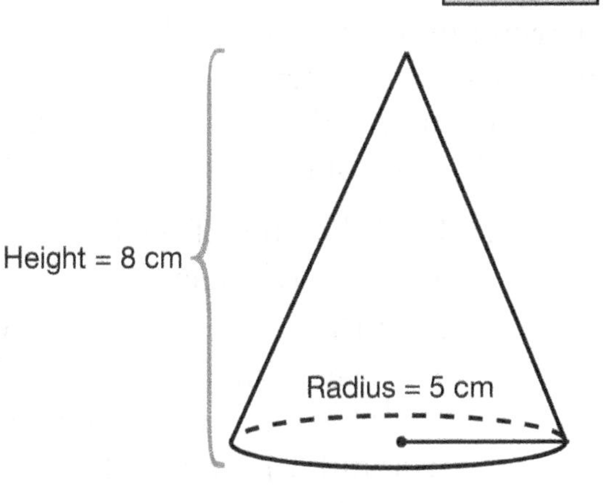

1. Find the area of the base by solving for the area of a circle: $A = \pi \times r^2$.
2. Find the volume by multiplying? times the area of the base times the height: $V = {}^1/_2 \times A \times h$. Record the volume of the cone shown above.
3. PRACTICE: Find the volume of the cone with height 8 cm and radius 4 cm. Contrast your answer with the volume you found for the cylinder with the same dimensions. What is the difference in volume? Does this make sense?

7 Calculating the volume for a rectangular pyramid

A pyramid looks like a cone. It has height and a rectangular base. The volume of the rectangular pyramid is found by multiplying $^1/_2$ times the area of the base times the height.

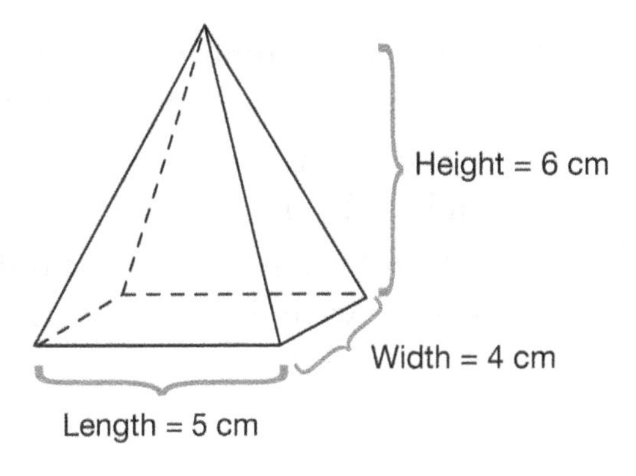

1. Find the area of the base by multiplying the length times the width: $A = l \times w$.
2. Find the volume by multiplying $^1/_3$ times the area of the base times the height: $V = {}^1/_3 \times A \times h$. Record the volume of the rectangular pyramid shown above.
3. PRACTICE: Find the volume of a rectangular pyramid with height 10 cm and width 4 cm and length 5 cm.
4. EXTRA CHALLENGE: If a rectangular pyramid had a height of 8 cm and a width of 4 cm, what length would it need to have to give the same volume as the cone in practice question 4 above?

8 Calculating volume for a triangular pyramid

A triangular pyramid is like a rectangular pyramid, but its base is a triangle. Find the area of the base first. Then calculate the volume by multiplying $^1/_3$ times the area of the base times the height.

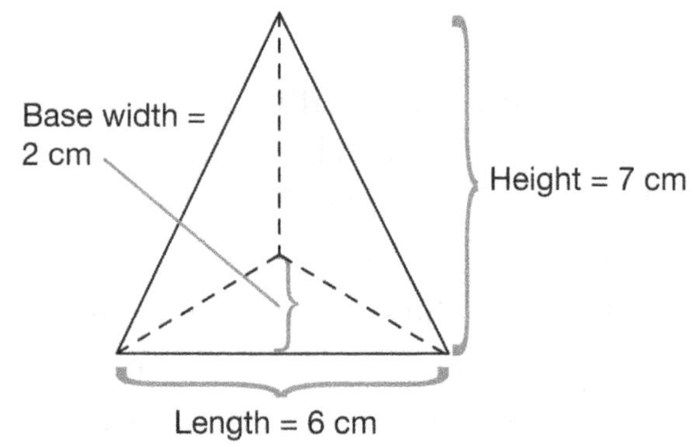

1. Find the area of the base by solving for the area of a triangle: $B = {}^1/_2 \times l \times w$.
2. Find the volume by multiplying $^1/_3$ times the area of the base times the height: $V = {}^1/_3 \times A \times h$. Find the volume of the triangular pyramid shown above.
3. PRACTICE: Find the volume of the triangular pyramid with height 10 cm and width 6 cm and length 5 cm.

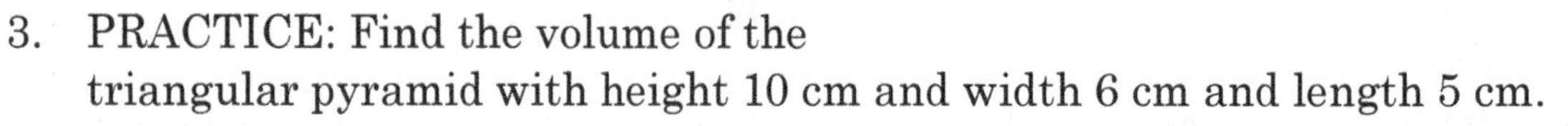

9 Calculating volume for a sphere

To find the volume of a sphere, you only need to know one dimension about the sphere, its radius.

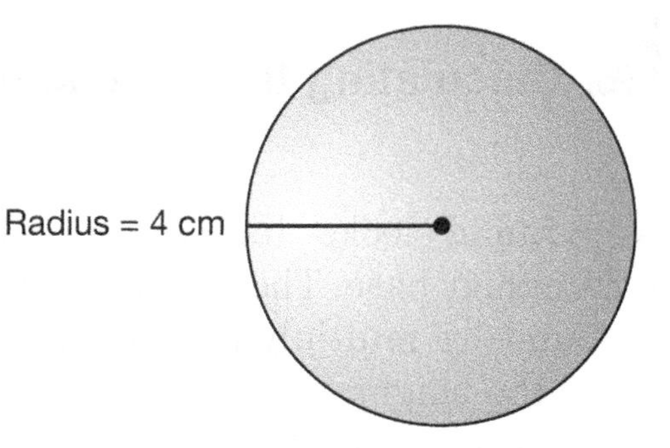

1. Find the volume of a sphere: $V = {}^4/_3 \pi r^3$. Find the volume for the sphere shown above.
2. PRACTICE: Find the volume for a sphere with radius 2 cm.
3. EXTRA CHALLENGE: Find the volume for a sphere with diameter 10 cm.

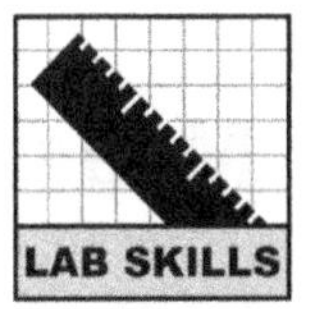

Measuring Volume

How do you find the volume of an irregular object?

It's easy to find the volume of a shoebox or a basketball. You just take a few measurements, plug the numbers into a math formula, and you have figured it out. But what if you want to find the volume of a bumpy rock, or an acorn, or a house key? There aren't any simple math formulas to help you out. However, there's an easy way to find the volume of an irregular object, as long the object is waterproof!

Materials

- Displacement tank
- Water source
- Disposable cup
- Beaker
- Graduated cylinder
- Sponges or paper towel
- Object to be measured

1 Setting up the displacement tank

Set the displacement tank on a level surface. Place a disposable cup under the tank's spout. Carefully fill the tank until the water begins to drip out of the spout. When the water stops flowing, discard the water collected in the disposable cup. Set the cup aside and place a beaker under the spout.

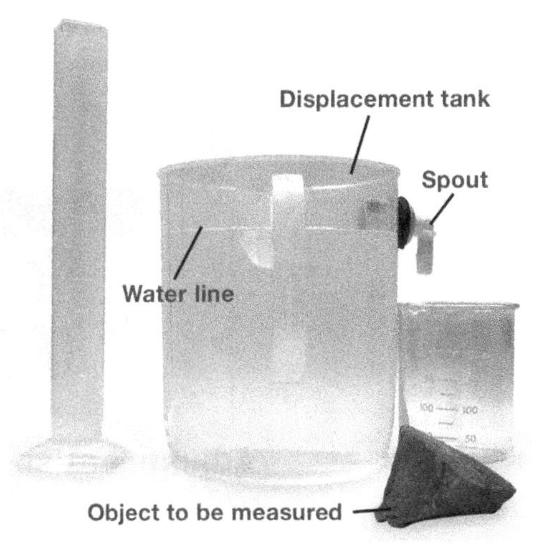

2 Stop and think

a. What do you think will happen when you place an object into the tank?

b. Which object would cause more water to come out of the spout, an acorn or a fist-sized rock?

c. Why are we interested in how much water comes out of the spout?

d. Explain how the displacement tank measures volume.

3 Measuring volume with the displacement tank

1. Gently place a waterproof object into the displacement tank. It is important to avoid splashing the water or creating a wave that causes extra water to flow out of the spout. It may take a little practice to master this step.

2. When the water stops flowing out of the spout, it can be poured from the beaker into a graduated cylinder for precise measurement. The volume of the water displaced is equal to the object's volume.
   Note: Occasionally, when a small object is placed in the tank, no water will flow out. This happens because an air bubble has formed in the spout. Simply tap the spout with a pencil to release the air bubble.

3. If you wish to measure the volume of another object, don't forget to refill the tank with water first!

Measuring Mass with a Triple Beam Balance

How do you find the mass of an object?

Why can't you use a bathroom scale to measure the mass of a paperclip? You could if you were finding the mass of a lot of them at one time! To find the mass of objects less than a kilogram you will need to use the triple beam balance.

Materials

- Triple beam balance
- Small objects
- Mass set (optional)
- Beaker

1 Parts of the triple beam balance

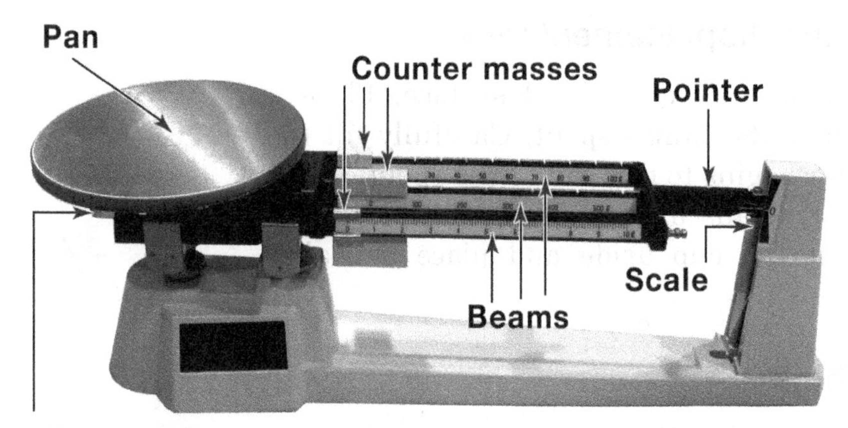

2 Setting up and zeroing the balance

The triple beam balance works like a see-saw. When the mass of your object is perfectly balanced by the counter masses on the beam, the pointer will rest at 0. Add up the readings on the three beams to find the mass of your object. The unit of measure for this triple beam balance is grams.

1. Place the balance on a level surface.
2. Clean any objects or dust off the pan.
3. Move all counter masses to 0. The pointer should rest at 0. Use the adjustment screw to adjust the pointer to 0, if necessary. When the pointer rests at 0 with no objects on the pan, the balance is said to be zeroed.

3 Finding a known mass

You can check that the triple beam balance is working correctly by using a mass set. Your teacher will provide the correct mass value for these objects.

1. After zeroing the balance, place an object with a known mass on the pan.
2. Move the counter masses to the right one at a time from largest to smallest. When the pointer is resting at 0 the numbers under the three counter masses should add up to the known mass.
3. If the pointer is above or below 0, recheck the balance set up. Recheck the position of the counter masses. Counter masses must be properly seated in a groove. Check with your teacher to make sure you are getting the correct mass before finding the mass an unknown object.

4 Finding the mass of an unknown object

1. After zeroing the balance, place an object with an unknown mass on the pan. Do not place hot objects or chemicals directly on the pan
2. Move the largest counter mass first. Place it in the first notch after zero. Wait until the pointer stops moving. If the pointer is above 0, move the counter mass to the next notch. Continue to move the counter mass to the right, one notch at a time until the pointer is slightly above 0. Go to step 3. If the pointer is below 0, move the counter mass back one notch. When the pointer rests at 0, you do not need to move any more counter masses.
3. Move the next largest counter mass from 0 to the first notch. Watch to see where the pointer rests. If it rests above 0, move the counter mass to the next notch. Repeat until the point rests at 0, or slightly above. If the pointer is slightly above 0, go to step 4.
4. Move the smallest counter mass from 0 to the position on the beam where the pointer rests at 0.
5. Add the masses from the three beams to get the mass of the unknown object. You should be able to record a number for the hundreds place, the tens place, the ones place, and the tenths place and the hundredths place. The hundredths place can be read to 0.00 or 0.05. You may have zeros in your answer.

5 Reading the balance correctly

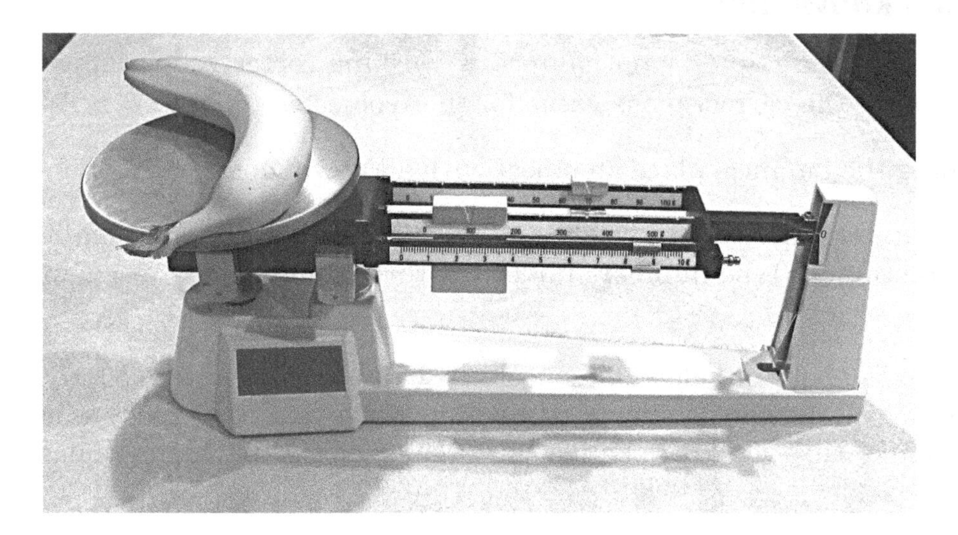

Look at the picture above. To find the mass of the object, locate the counter mass on each beam. Read the numbers directly below each counter mass. You can read the smallest mass to 0.05 grams. Write down the three numbers. Add them together. Report your answer in grams. Does your answer agree with others? If not, check your mass values from each beam to find your mistake.

6 Finding the mass of an object in a container

To measure the mass of a liquid or powder you will need an empty container on the pan to hold the sample. You must find the mass of the empty container first. After you place the object in the container and find the total mass, you can subtract the container's mass from the total to find the object's mass.

1. After zeroing the balance, place a beaker on the pan.
2. Follow directions for finding the mass of an unknown object. Record the mass of the beaker.
3. Place a small object in the beaker.
4. Move the counter masses to the right, largest to smallest, to find the total mass.
5. Subtract the beaker's mass from the total mass. This is the mass of your object in grams.

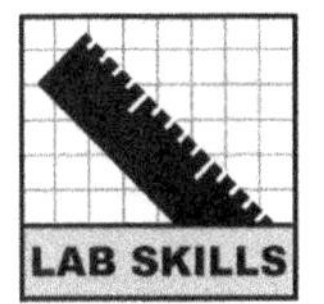

Recording Observations in the Lab

How do you record valid observations for an experiment in the lab?

When you perform an experiment you will be making important observations. You and others will use these observations to test a hypothesis. In order for an experiment to be valid, the evidence you collect must be objective and repeatable. This investigation will give you practice making and recording good observations.

Materials

- Paper
- Pencil
- Calculator
- Ruler

1 Making valid observations

Valid scientific observations are objective and repeatable. Scientific observations are limited to one's senses and the equipment used to make these observations. An objective observation means that the observer describes only what happened. The observer uses data, words, and pictures to describe the observations as exactly as possible. An experiment is repeatable if other scientists can see or repeat the same result. The following exercise gives you practice identifying good scientific observations.

2 Exercise 1

1. **Which observation is the most objective? Circle the correct letter.**
   a. My frog died after 3 days in the aquarium. I miss him.
   b. The frog died after 3 days in the aquarium. We will test the temperature and water conditions to find out why.
   c. Frogs tend to die in captivity. Ours did after three days.
2. **Which observation is the most descriptive? Circle the correct letter.**
   a. After weighing 3.000 grams of sodium bicarbonate into an Erlenmeyer flask, we slowly added 50.0 milliliters of vinegar. The contents of the flask began to bubble.
   b. We weighed the powder into a glass container. We added acid. It bubbled a lot.
   c. We saw a fizzy reaction.

3. **Which experiment has enough detail to repeat? Circle the correct letter.**
   a. Each student took a swab culture from his or her teeth. The swab was streaked onto nutrient agar plates and incubated at 37 C.
   b. Each student received a nutrient agar plate and a swab. Each student performed a swab culture of his or her teeth. The swab was streaked onto the agar plate. The plates were stored face down in the 37 C incubator and checked daily for growth. After 48 hours the plates were removed from the incubator and each student recorded his or her results.
   c. Each student received a nutrient agar plate and a swab. Each student performed a swab culture of his or her teeth. The swab was streaked onto the agar plate. The plates were stored face down in the 37 C incubator and checked daily for growth. After 48 hours the plates were removed from the incubator and each student counted the number of colonies present on the surface of the agar.

3 Recording valid observations

As a part of your investigations you will be asked to record observations on a skill sheet or in the results section of a lab report. There are different ways to show your observations. Here are some examples:

1. **Short description:** Use descriptive words to explain what you did or saw. Write complete sentences. Give as much detail as possible about the experiment. Try to answer the following questions: What? Where? When? Why? and How?

2. **Tables:** Tables are a good way to display the data you have collected. Later, the data can be plotted on a graph. Be sure to include a title for the table, labels for the sets of data, and units for the values. Check values to make sure you have the correct number of significant figures.

Table 1: U.S. penny mass by year

Year manufactured	1977	1978	1979	1980	1981	1982	1983	1984	1985
Mass (grams)	3.0845	3.0921	3.0689	2.9915	3.0023	2.5188	2.5042	2.4883	2.5230

3. **Graphs and charts:** A graph or chart is a picture of your data. There are different kinds of graphs and charts: line graphs, trend charts, bar graphs, and pie graphs, for example. A line graph is shown below.

   Label the important parts of your graph. Give your graph a title. The x-axis and y-axis should have labels for the data, the unit values, and the number range on the graph.

   The line graph in the example has a straight line through the data. Sometimes data does not fit a straight line. Often scientists will plot data first in a trend chart to see how the data looks. Check with your instructor if you are unsure how to display your data.

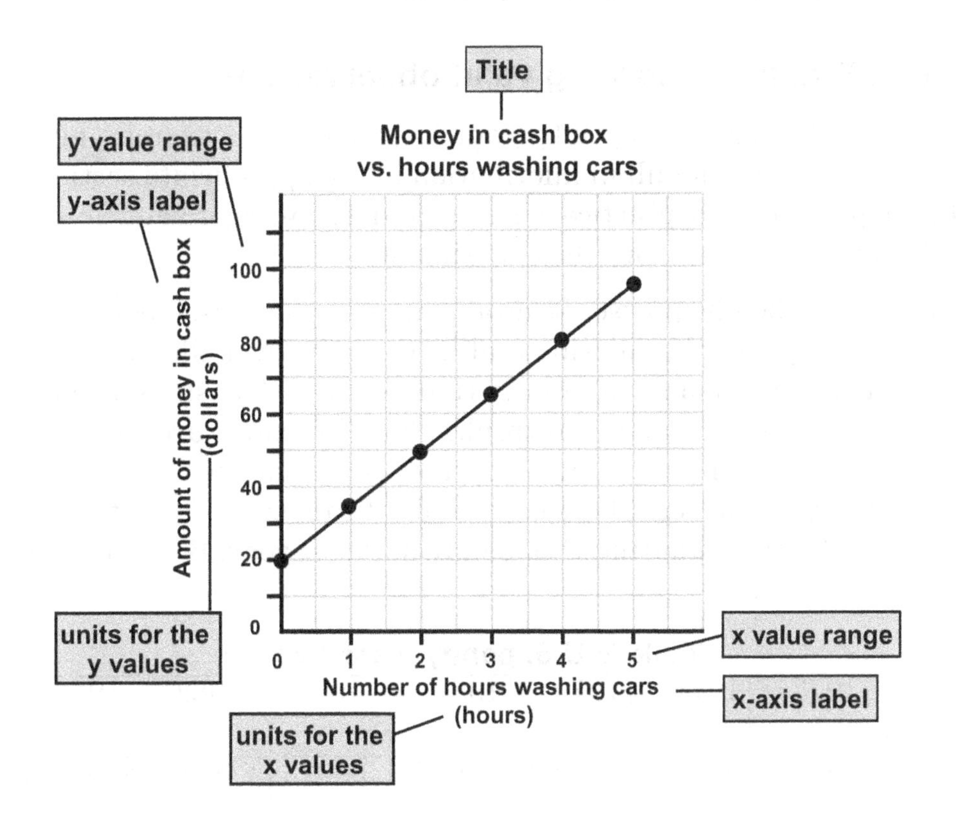

4. **Drawings:** Sometimes you will record observations by drawing a sketch of what you see. The example below was observed under a microscope.

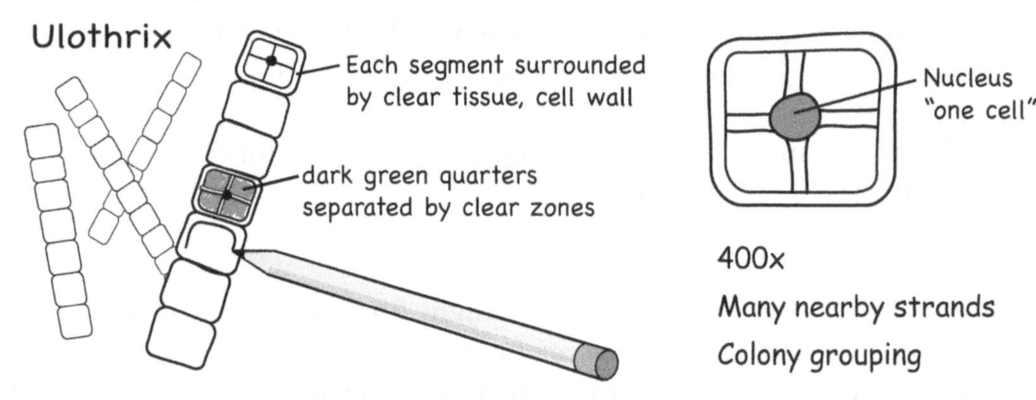

Give the name of the specimen. Draw enough detail to make the sketch look realistic. Use color, when possible. Identify parts of the object you were asked to observe. Provide the magnification or size of the image.

4 Exercise 2: Practice recording valid observations

A lab report form has been given to you by your instructor. This exercise gives you a chance to read through an experiment and fill in information in the appropriate sections of the lab report form. Use this opportunity to practice writing and graphing scientific observations. Then answer the following questions about the experiment.

A student notices that when he presses several pennies in a pressed penny machine, his brand new penny has some copper color missing and he can see silver-like material underneath. He wonders, "Are some pennies made differently than others?" The student has a theory that not all U.S. pennies are made the same. He thinks that if pennies are made differently now he might be able to find out when the change occurred. He decides to collect a U.S. penny for each year from 1977 to the present, record the date, and take its mass. The student records the data in a table and creates a graph plotting U.S. penny mass vs. year. Below is a table of some of his data:

Table 2: U.S. penny mass by year

Year manufactured	1977	1978	1979	1980	1981	1982	1983	1984	1985
Mass (grams)	3.0845	3.0921	3.0689	2.9915	3.0023	2.5188	2.5042	2.4883	2.5230

5 Stop and think

a. What observation did the student make first before he began his experiment?

b. How did the student display his observations?

c. In what section of the lab report did you show observations?

d. What method did you use to display the observations? Explain why you chose this one.

Physics Stand

You will need:

- Physics Stand pole
- Physics Stand washer
- Physics Stand base
- Physics Stand bolt

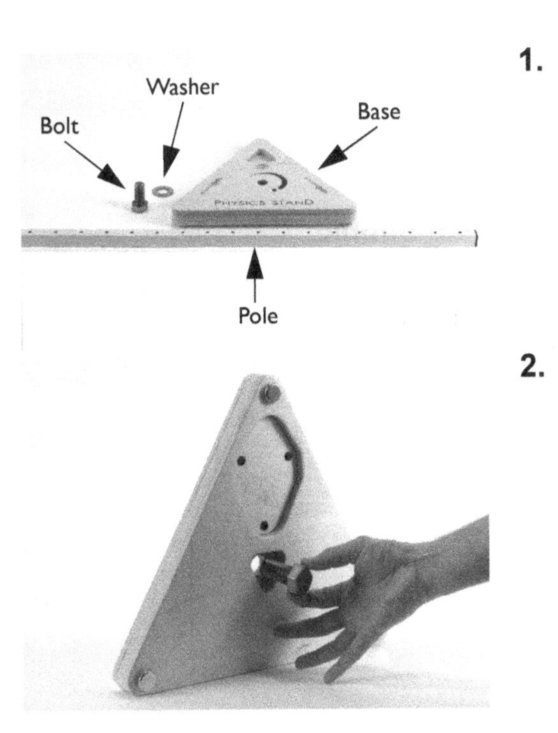

1. **Identifying the parts of the physics stand**

   There are four parts to the physics stand; the base, the pole, the washer and the bolt.

2. **Placing the bolt into the base**

   From the bottom of the base slide the large bolt through the hole.

3. **Sliding the washer onto the bolt**

   Be sure to push the bolt into the cut-out triangle on the bottom of the stand. The washer will fit over the threaded part of the bolt.

4. **Attaching the pole to the base**

   The pole screws onto the threads of the bolt. The bolt will not spin when you hold the bolt into the cut-out triangle on the bottom of the base. Spin the pole until it screws down snug onto the washer.

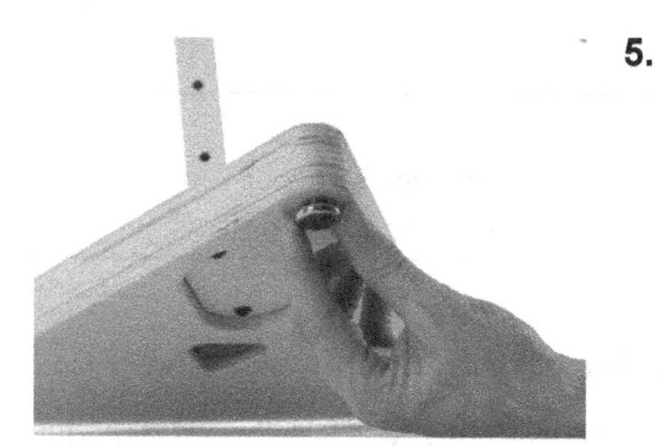

5. **Leveling the stand**

There are three adjustable feet on the bottom of the base. These feet screw into the base. They can be extended by unscrewing them a few turns.

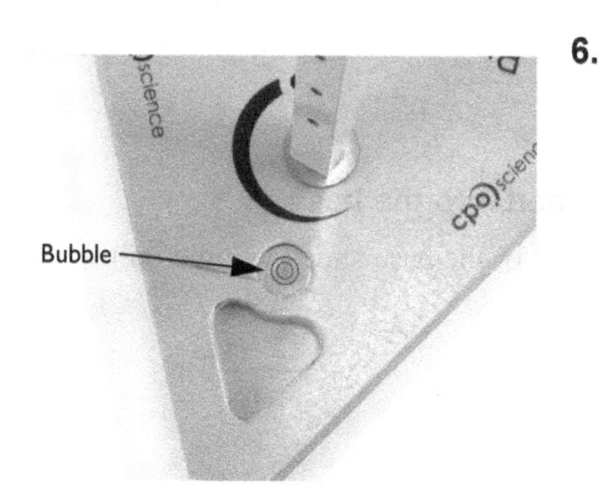

6. **Using the leveling bubble**

When the bubble is directly in the center of the small circle, the stand is level. By adjusting the feet on the bottom of the base by small amounts, the stand can be brought into level.

Car and Ramp

You will need:

- Physics Stand assembly
- Weights
- Car
- Foot
- Ramp
- Black plastic knob

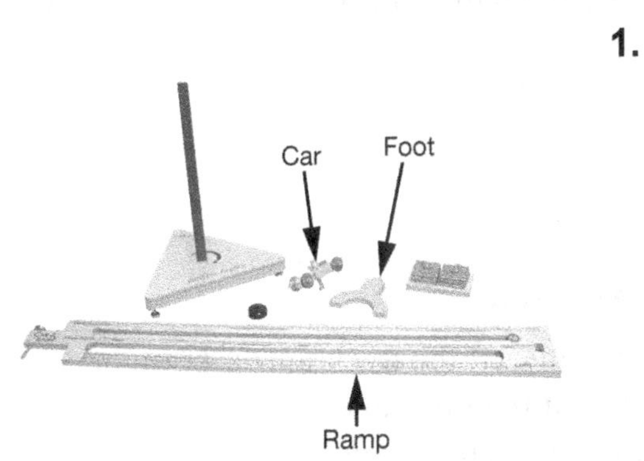

1. **Identifying the parts of the Car and Ramp**

   The Car and Ramp come in three pieces; the car, the ramp, and the foot.

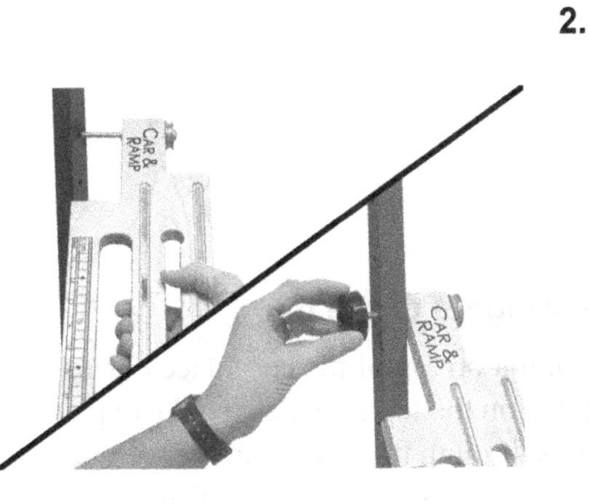

2. **Attaching the Ramp to the stand.**

   Place the threaded rod on the end of the ramp through the desired hole in the stand. Secure the ramp to the stand with the black plastic knob.

3. **Attaching the foot to the ramp.**

   The foot is optional. It is put in place by sliding the tab at the top of the foot into the hole at the bottom of the ramp. The foot will support the lower portion of the ramp.

4. **Putting the car on the ramp.**

The car is set onto the ramp by guiding the head of the large screw on the bottom of the car through a hole at the top of the ramp. Once the screw head fits through, the wheels of the car will line up with small grooves parallel to the long gap that runs the length of the track. The screw head will fit inside this gap as the car goes down the ramp and will not touch the sides and impede the car down the track.

5. **Secured to the track.**

The car will not come off the track unless brought back up to the top of the track and the screw head guided out of the hole. This keeps the car securely on the track, with no chance of flying off once it hits the bottom.

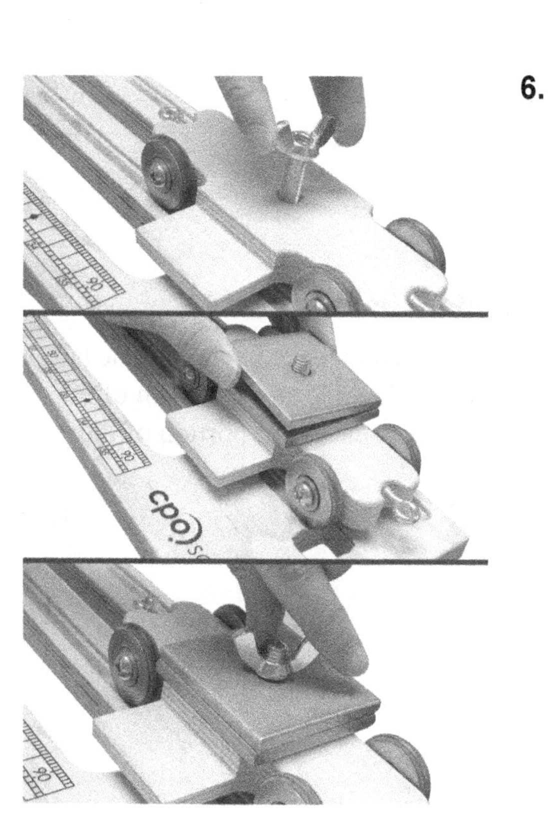

6. **Securing the weights to the car.**

Remove the wingnut on top of the car. Place desired number of weights on the top of the car so the exposed threaded rod goes through the hole(s) in the weight(s). Attach wingnut on top of threaded rod to firmly secure weights to car.

Ropes and Pulleys

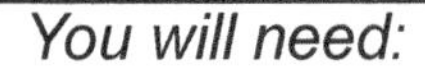

- Physics Stand assembly
- 1 set of weights
- Tape measure
- Upper and lower pulley blocks attached by red safety string
- 1 set of spring scales
- Blue knob
- Yellow string with cord stops
- Black knob

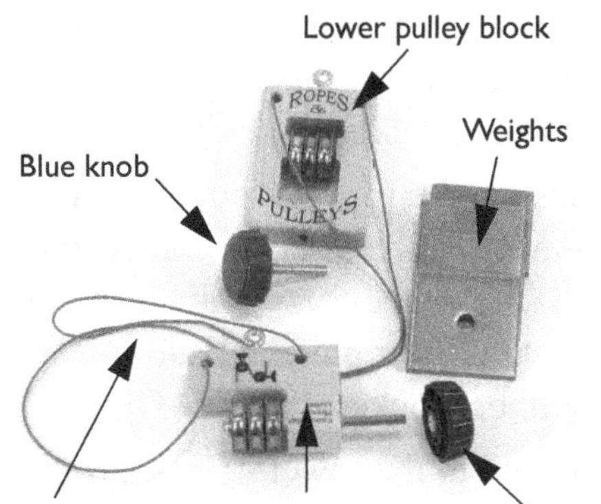

1. Identifying the parts of the ropes and pulleys

The ropes and pulleys set is an ideal way to learn the basic principles behind how simple machines work. The upper and lower pulley blocks each contain three pulleys. The number of pulleys through which the string passes can be varied by passing the string through the desired number. The force of the bottom pulley block can be varied by adding or subtracting weights. The pulleys contain low friction bearings for accurate force measurements.

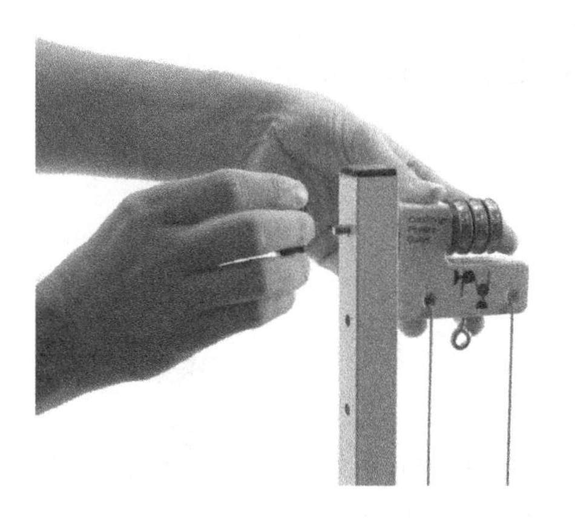

2. Attaching the upper pulley block

Slide the threaded rod attached to the upper pulley block through the top hole of the physics stand. Secure the pulley block with the black knob. You should now have the upper pulley block secured, while the lower pulley block hangs below on the two red safety strings.

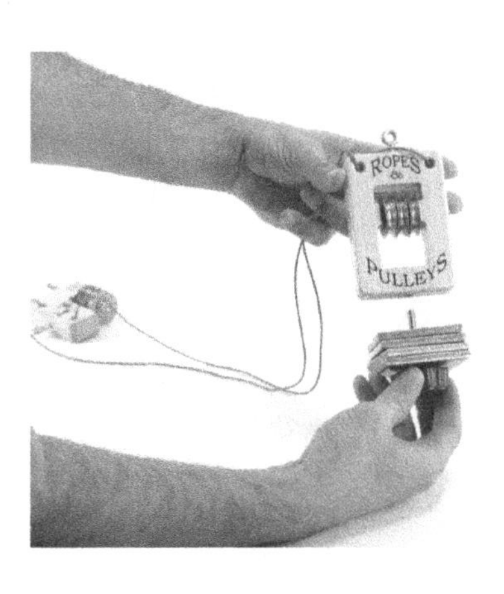

3. Weighing the bottom block

Add weights to the bottom block using the blue knob with the threaded stud. Slide the threaded stud through the hole in the weight and screw it into the bottom of the lower pulley.

After the weights have been secured, weigh the lower pulley block by hanging it onto a spring scale using the eyelet on top.

4. **Stringing the pulley blocks**

The yellow string is the one you will use to move the lower pulley block up and down. The red strings are the safety strings that hold the bottom block while you arrange the yellow strings. The cord stops are used as reference markers for measuring the length of string needed to raise the lower block a given distance.

The first step to stringing the ropes & pulleys is to choose where to connect the brass clip on the end of the yellow string. The clip can either be attached to the upper pulley block or the lower pulley block using the eyelet on either block.

If the string is connected to the lower pulley block a mechanical advantage of 1, 3 or 5 can be obtained (1, 3, or 5 supporting strings). The diagram to the right shows a mechanical advantage of 1.

Connect string to the lower pulley block for mechanical advantage of 1,3, or 5.

If the string is connected to the upper pulley block a mechanical advantage of 2, 4, or 6 can be obtained (2, 4, or 6 supporting strings). The diagram to the right shows a mechanical advantage of 2.

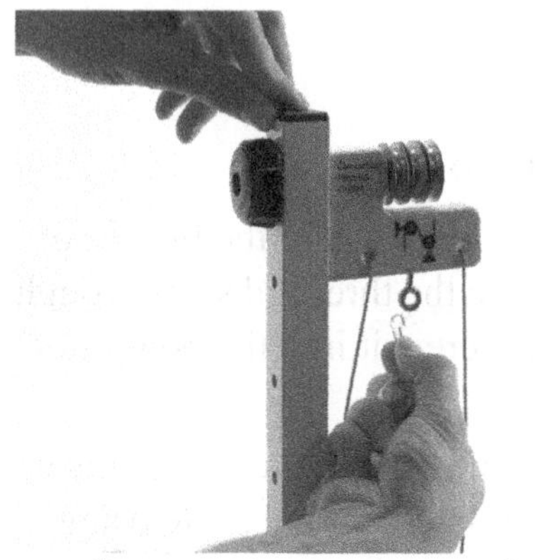

Connect string to the upper pulley block for mechanical advantage of 2,4, or 6.

Electric Circuits

You will need:

- Electric circuits table
- 6 light bulbs and 3 holders
- 2 brown (long-length) wires
- 1 red (20-ohm) resistor
- 1 potentiometer
- 6 green (short-length) wires
- 2 green (5-ohm) resistors
- 2 knife switches
- 2 battery holders
- 2 blue (medium-length) wires
- 1 blue (10-ohm) resistor

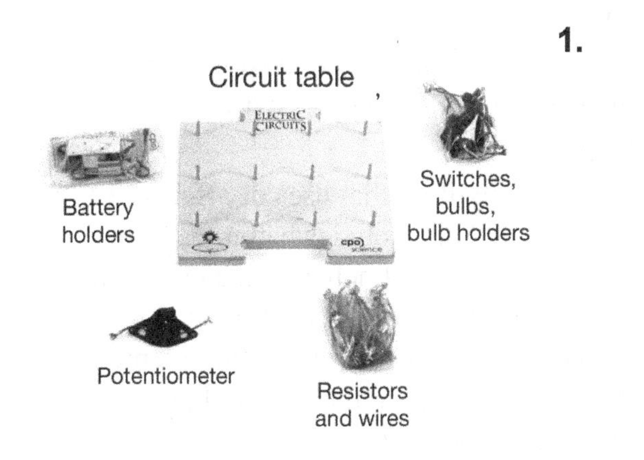

1. Identifying the parts of the electric circuits kit.

The electric circuits table is a wooden platform with brass posts for securely assembling electric circuits. There are 12 brass posts used in making connections between different components of the circuit

The posts are not connected underneath and there are no hidden wires. All connections are made using wires that come in a separate pack.

Circuits are made with wires, batteries, bulbs and holders, resistors, and switches.

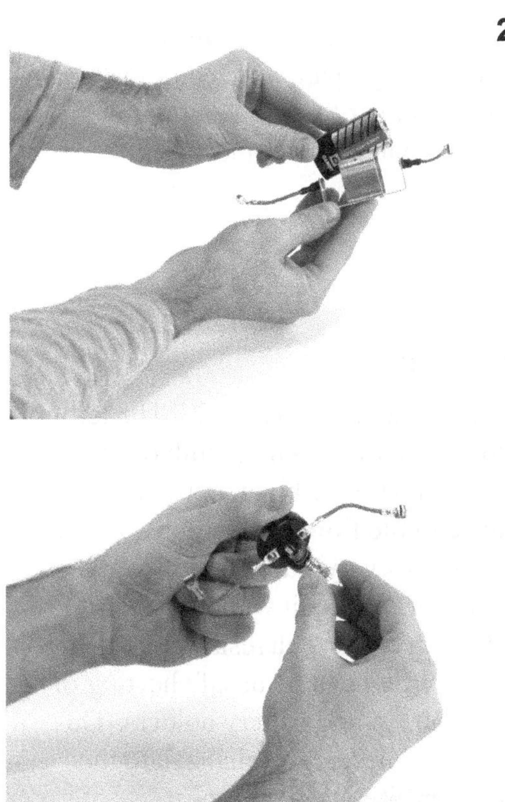

2. Assembling the components.

Place D batteries (1.5 volts) into the battery holders.

Place a light bulb into each bulb holder.

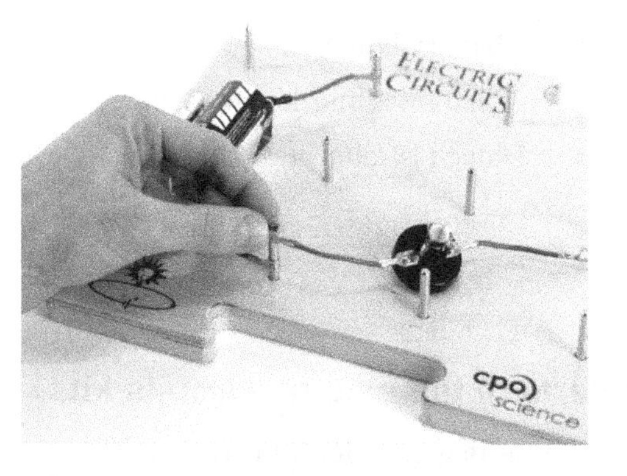

3. **Adding wires and circuit elements.**

Each wire has a circular connector at both ends called a hoop connector. To add a wire to the board, just place the hoop around the post and push down on the hoop. It will slide down the post, like a jewelry ring over a finger. If you need to add one or more wires to the post, simply push the first wire down the post to make room for another hoop. You can add up to 4 hoops to a post.

NOTE: Solid contact is made at any position on the post. It is not necessary to slide every wire to the bottom of the post.

A circuit element is any item that uses or affects electricity in a circuit. This includes batteries, light bulbs, resistors and switches. Each circuit element that comes with the kit has the same type of hoop connectors as the wires. To connect a circuit element to a post just place the hoop on the post and push down, sliding it down the post.

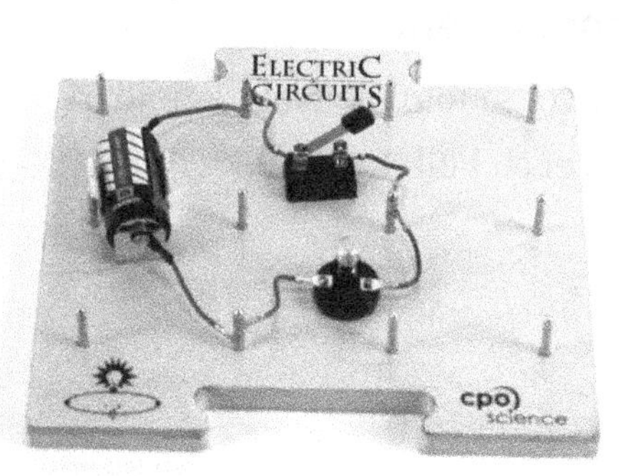

4. **Closing the circuit.**

A circuit is made when wires and elements are connected together making a path for electricity. Shown at left is an example of a simple circuit with a battery, a light bulb, a switch, and some wires.

5. **Avoiding short circuits.**

Circuits should always include a “resistor.” The term “resistor” refers to a device like a light bulb or one of the resistors that comes with the kit and provides a substantial resistance to the flow of electricity. A wire alone in a circuit provides very little resistance and is not considered a resistor. A circuit without a resistor, or one in which a branch bypasses a resistor, is called a short circuit. A *short circuit* causes unsafe heating of connecting wires, batteries, and battery holders. This could result in burns and irreparable damage to the equipment. Avoid short circuits at all times!

Pendulum

You will need:

- Physics Stand assembly
- Pendulum bob and string assembly
- Pendulum face
- 10 washers
- 2 blue knobs with threaded stud
- Timer and photogates

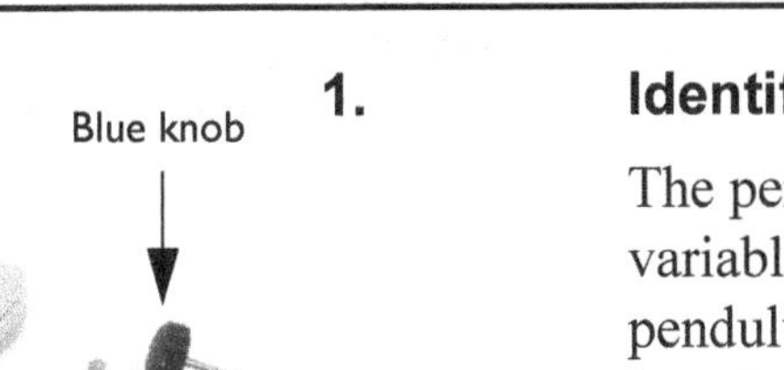
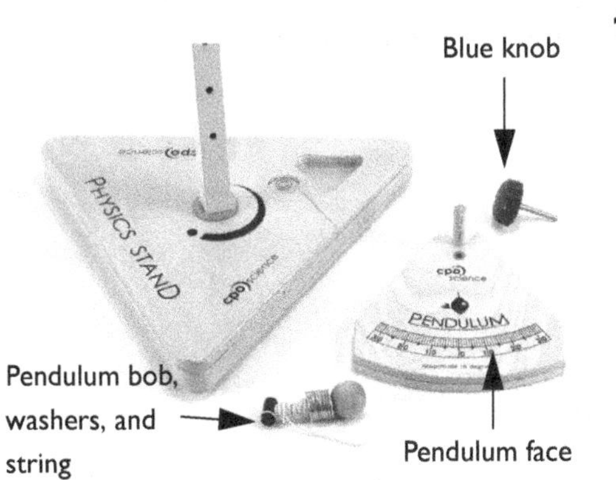

1. Identifying the parts of the pendulum.

The pendulum experiment allows you to change three variables: the length of the string, the mass of the pendulum, and the angle of the swing (amplitude). The length of the string can be varied from 15 cm to nearly 1 meter. The pendulum has a hardwood face with an angle scale for easy determination of the amplitude. Washers can be added to or subtracted from the pendulum bob to change the mass.

2. Attaching the pendulum face to the physics stand.

Slide the threaded stud on the blue knob through the desired hole in the physics stand.

Turn the blue knob to thread the stud into the back of the pendulum face, securing it to the physics stand.

3. Attaching the pendulum bob and string

Select the length of string for the pendulum bob by sliding the string into the slot in the peg on the pendulum face. Check the length of the string by measuring from the bottom of the slotted peg to the bottom of the stack of washers on the pendulum bob. You can add or subtract washers from the pendulum bob to change the mass.

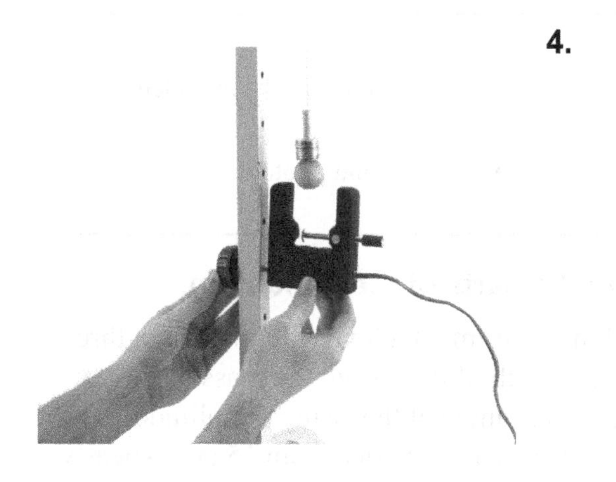

4. **Mounting the photogate to the physics stand.**

To mount the photogate to the physics stand, you will need another blue knob with threaded stud. Place the outer edge of the photogate to against the hole that allows you to align the opening with the pendulum bob. Do not overtighten. Make sure the pendulum bob breaks the beam in the photogate each time it swings.

5. **Aligning the photogate**

Be sure to align the two small holes in the photogate with the center of the round portion of the pendulum bob.

Attach the photogate to slot A in the timer using the red or blue wire. Be sure the "A" light is on and that the timer is set to period mode.

Atom Building Game

You will need:

- Atom game board
- 1 tube yellow marbles
- Laminated periodic table
- 1 tube blue marbles
- Nuclear Reactions cards
- Game booklet
- 1 tube red marbles
- Photons and Lasers cards

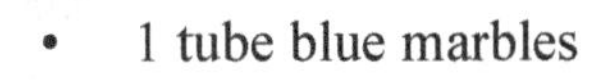

1. Identifying the parts of the game.

The Atom Building Game comes with an atom game board, blue, red, and yellow marbles, game cards, a laminated periodic table, and an instruction booklet.

The game cards include Nuclear Reactions cards and Photons and Lasers cards. You will learn how to use these cards in the Investigations.

Energy levels

Nucleus

Marble Pocket

2. Using the atom game board.

The Atom game board is designed to sit on a table top with four players (or teams) around it. Each player (or team) is assigned to one of the four marble pockets.

The center of the board represents the nucleus. This is where the protons (red marbles) and neutrons (blue marbles) are place during the activities.

The steps around the nucleus represent the energy levels that are occupied by the electrons (yellow marbles).

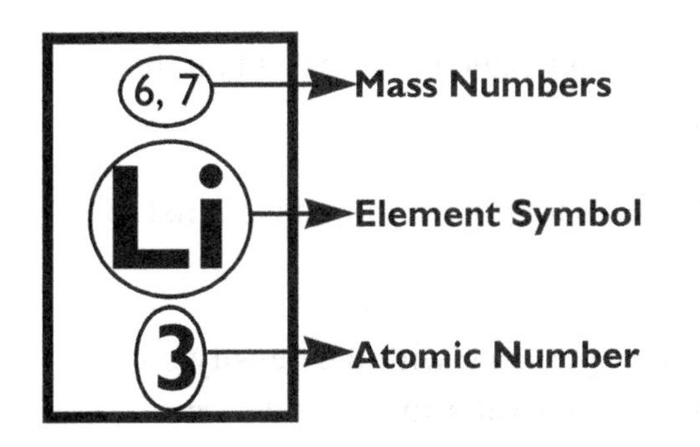

3. Using the periodic table.

The periodic table is used for many of the activities. The atomic number is the number of protons (red marbles) in the nucleus.

The atomic number determines what element the atom is. The mass number is the total number of particles (protons plus neutrons) in the nucleus.

Isotopes are atoms with the same number of protons but different numbers of neutrons. You can figure out the number of neutrons by subtracting the atomic number from the mass number. For example, lithium-6 has 3 protons and 3 neutrons (6 - 3 = 3).

Neutral atoms have the same number of electrons as protons. The atom in step 2 is lithium-6.

The Density of Water

Is the density of solid and liquid water different?

Water is important and life as we know it can't exist without it. Water also plays an important role in Earth's weather, climate, and shaping it's surface. Water exists in massive quantities in the oceans, in the polar ice caps, in surface fresh water, and in underground aquifers and rivers. Water has some interesting and unusual qualities. In this investigation, you will compare and contrast the density of water in its liquid and solid form.

Materials

- Density cubes
- 50 mL graduated cylinder (plastic)
- Electronic scale or triple-beam balance
- Displacement tank
- Metric ruler
- Ice cube

1 Finding the density of liquid water

You have completed two investigations so far on calculating the density of various materials. Use what you have learned about calculating density to calculate the density of liquid water. You will freeze a small amount of liquid water and use it in its solid form to calculate the density of ice.

1. Follow your teacher's directions and label your graduated cylinder.
2. Measure the mass of your graduated cylinder and record its mass in Table 1.
3. Pour between 35 and 40 mL of water into your graduated cylinder. Record this volume in Table 1.
4. Measure the mass of the graduated cylinder with the water in it. Record this mass in Table 1.
5. Calculate the mass of the water in your graduated cylinder and record it in Table 1.
6. Calculate the density of water and record it in Table 1.
7. Follow your teacher's directions and set your labeled graduated cylinder aside so it can be frozen. Be careful not to spill your water.

Table 1: Mass, volume, and density of liquid water

Mass of graduated cylinder (g)	Mass of graduated cylinder filled with water (g)	Mass of water in graduated cylinder (g)	Volume of water in graduated cylinder (g)	Density of water in cylinder (g/mL)

2 Thinking about density and buoyancy

a. When you predicted whether the density cubes would float in water, you came up with a rule to help you make your predictions. What was the rule you came up with?

b. Think about situations where you have seen ice in water in your life. With your group make a list of these situations. In these situations, did the ice sink or float?

c. Based on your observations of how ice behaved in water, and your experience with the density cubes and your clay boat you made, make a prediction about the density of ice (water in its solid form) compared to the density of liquid water.

d. How could you test this prediction?

3 Designing an experiment

Think about how you used the density cubes to predict whether they would sink of float. Design an experiment that uses the density cubes to see if you can predict the density of ice. Make observations about how the various density cubes sink or float in water. You can use the displacement tank to perform your experiment.

a. Brainstorm with your group ideas about how you can use the density cubes and the displacement tank to predict the density of ice.

b. Describe how you will gather data and make observations. Include diagrams and drawings with labels or explanations of what they represent.

c. Describe how you will use your data and observations to make your prediction. Be sure to state how accurate your prediction will be to the actual density of ice.

d. Describe any method you can think of to test your prediction.

e. Once you have all your ideas together, write up a plan for your experiment. List the materials you will use, the process you will follow, and show the data tables you will use. See if you can include a small section that discusses if the prediction you made in part 2d was correct or not, and why.

f. Show your plan to your teacher for discussion. Once it is approved, try your experiment and make your prediction about the density of ice.

4 Stop and think

a. What was your prediction for the density of ice?

b. Was your prediction for 2d correct or incorrect? How could you tell?

c. Do you think the size, shape, or mass of a piece of ice changes it's density? Why or not?

5 Finding the density of ice

1. Find your group's graduated cylinder. It will now have solid water - ice - in it.
2. Record the mass of your graduated cylinder from Table 1 in Table 2.
3. Measure and record in Table 2 the mass of the graduated cylinder with the ice in it.
4. Calculate the mass of the ice in your graduated cylinder and record it in Table 2.
5. Calculate the density of ice and record it in Table 2.

Table 2: Mass, volume, and density of ice

Mass of graduated cylinder (g)	Mass of graduated cylinder filled with ice (g)	Mass of ice in graduated cylinder (g)	Volume of ice in graduated cylinder (g)	Density of ice in cylinder (g/mL)

6 Comparing the density of liquid water and ice

a. Did the mass of the water in your graduated cylinder change?

b. Did the volume of the water in your graduated cylinder change?

c. What affect did this have on the density?

d. How did the density of ice compare to the density of water? Does this explain the way you have observed ice to behave in water and what you know about density and buoyancy?

e. How did the density of the ice in your graduated cylinder compare to your prediction from part 4a?

f. What may have helped you make a better prediction?

7 Thinking about what you observed

a. Use the Internet or other reference materials to find the actual accepted value for the density of ice.

b. How does your prediction from 4a. compare to the actual density of ice? Calculate your percent error.

c. How does your calculated value of the density of the ice from Table 2 compare to the actual density of ice? Calculate the percent error.

d. Which value was closer to the actual density of ice, your prediction from 4a.or your calculated value from Table 2?

e. Why do you think it was closer to the actual density of ice?

f. Use the Internet or other reference materials to research ice. What is unusual about the density of liquid water compared to the density of solid water - ice?

Stars, Galaxies, and Dark Matter

What is the role of gravity in the motion and formation of galaxies?

Materials

- Scientific calculator

About thirteen billion years ago a cataclysmic explosion occurred and the universe started growing from a tiny point into the incredible vastness we now observe. In jest, someone called this beginning the "big bang" and the name stuck.

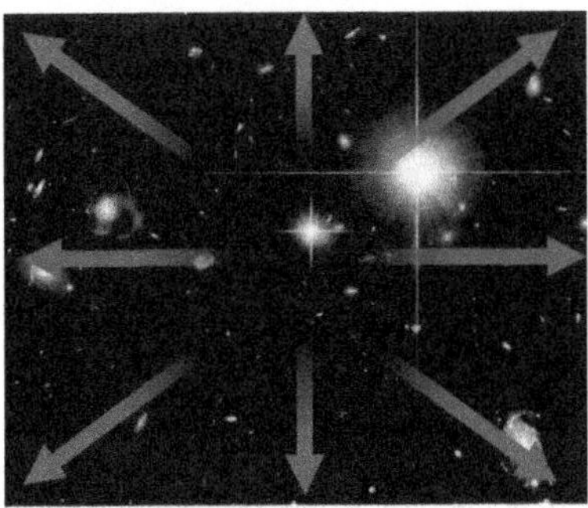

Photo courtesyNASA, ESA, and The Hubble Heritage Team (STScI/AURA)

We do see evidence for the big bang itself. The fact that galaxies are expanding away from each other (shown left) is a strong argument for the big bang. As far as we can look into the universe, we find galaxies are expanding away from each other. However, some galaxies like the Milky Way and the Andromeda galaxy are moving toward each other and will eventually merge to form one galaxy.

The focus of this Exploration is to "expand" your understanding of the role that gravity plays in the motion and formation of galaxies. In the process, you will learn about stars, dark energy, and dark matter. You will also learn about the role played by supercomputers in studying our huge and amazing universe. Do the following to answer the questions in this Exploration: work with a partner or team, conduct research on the Internet or in a library, discuss you ideas with your teacher, and talk to experts.

1 Stars

Stars are massive. The mass of our Sun, for example, makes up 99% of the mass of our solar system.

In chapter 7, you learned about Newton's law of universal gravitation. This law states that the strength of the gravitational force that acts between two objects depends on the mass of those objects and the distance between their centers. The formula for this law is below.

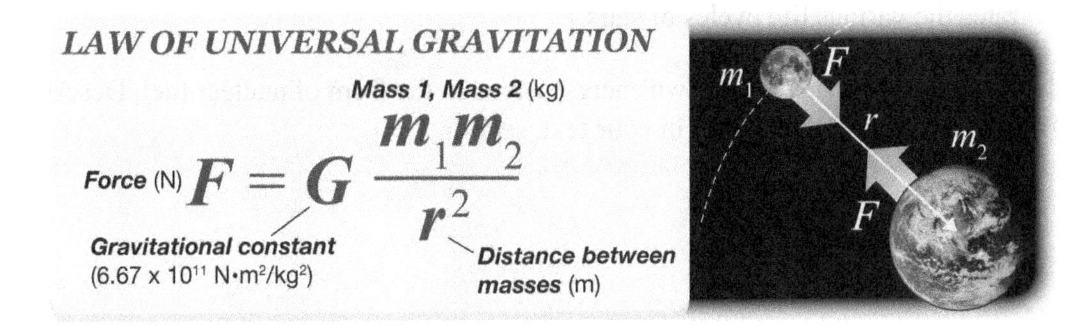

a. All objects that have mass attract each other through gravity. Use Newton's law of universal gravitation to calculate the gravitational force of attraction between you and an apple that is 10 meters away. You may use estimates for your and the apple's mass values.

b. All the planets in our solar system orbit the center of mass of our solar system. The center of mass is the balance point between the two objects. The value "*r*" in the law of universal gravitation is the sum of two distances: $d_1 + d_2$ where d_1 equals the distance from mass 1 to the center of mass between the two objects and d_2 equals the distance from mass 2 to the center of mass. With our Sun being so massive, where might the center of mass be for our solar system? Make a prediction and then research the correct answer.

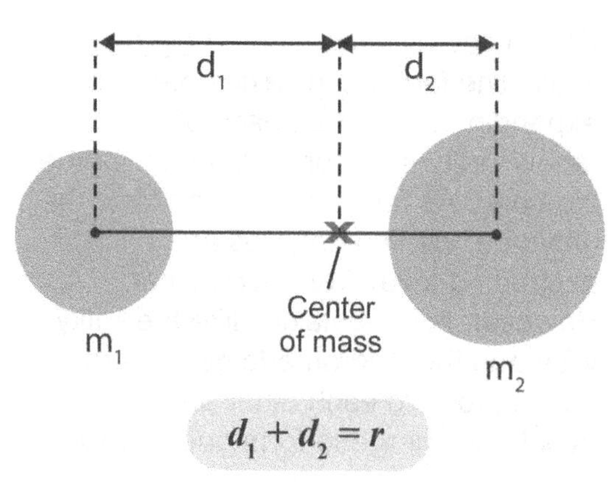

c. Recent studies have suggested that a black hole, with a mass of more than a million Suns, exists at the very center of our galaxy, the Milky Way. The evidence for this huge black hole comes from measurements of the orbital velocities of stars and gas at the center of the galaxy. In one study, an infrared telescope was used to measure the orbital velocities of 20 stars over a three-year period. It was determined that these stars were orbiting at velocities of up to 1,000 km/s. This extremely high orbital velocity requires an object with a mass that is over 2 million times that of the Sun. Research and describe the role of gravitational force in forming a black hole.

d. Stars have life cycles. The birth of a star happens in a nebula, which is a huge cloud of dust and gas. At the end of its life, a star may become a white dwarf, a neutron star, or a black hole. Our Sun is a medium-sized star in the middle of its life cycle. Betelgeuse, the second brightest star in the constellation Orion, is called a red supergiant. In which end-of-life stage will each of these end up, and why? What is the role of gravitational force in forming each end-of-life stage? [Hint: Find a diagram that illustrates the various life cycles of stars.]

e. Stars shine because they have their own energy source in the form of nuclear fuel. Describe this nuclear fuel. [Hint: You can find the answer in your text, section 7.3.]

2 Dark matter and dark energy

In Part 1, you learned that a black hole at the core of the Milky Way is so massive that it affects the velocities of stars that orbit it. Looking at the velocities of celestial objects is one way to tell what is happening in the universe. For example, look at the graph below.

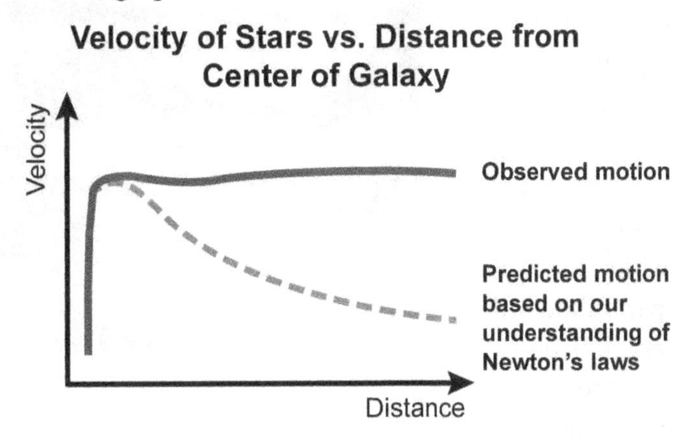

According to predictions based on our understanding of Newton's laws, the velocity of stars should decrease as they get near the edges of the galaxy. This is because the greatest concentration of "baryonic" matter in a galaxy is in the center (sort of like how our massive Sun is in the center of our solar system). Baryonic matter is composed of particles (such as protons and neutrons) and makes up most of the visible matter in the universe including stars, black holes, dust, and planets.

Because most of this visible matter is in the center, one would think that a star at the edge of a galaxy would feel less gravitational force and slow down. Similarly, planets that are most distance from the Sun orbit more slowly than planets nearby. For example, Mercury travels at 48 km/s whereas Neptune travels at about 5.4 km/s. However, the graph above shows that stars do not slow down at the edges of galaxies.

Scientists believe that dark matter is responsible for this observation. Dark matter is called the "missing mass" because in spite of being invisible it must be present to account for the motion of galaxies. In spite of knowing it's there, scientists have yet to detect dark matter because it so weakly interactive with other matter or with electromagnetic radiation. In fact, dark matter particles are called WIMPS (weakly interactive massive particles). Unlike, visible matter, dark matter is uniformly distributed through the universe. Its net effect on Earth is similar to its net effect on the Sun for this reason. So within our solar system (which is just a tiny part of the Milky Way), the velocities of planets slow down at greater distances from the Sun. However, a star at the edge of a galaxy experiences force from all the dark matter in the galaxy. This massive amount of dark matter also acts like a point of mass at the center of the galaxy and produces enough gravitational force to prevent the star from slowing down.

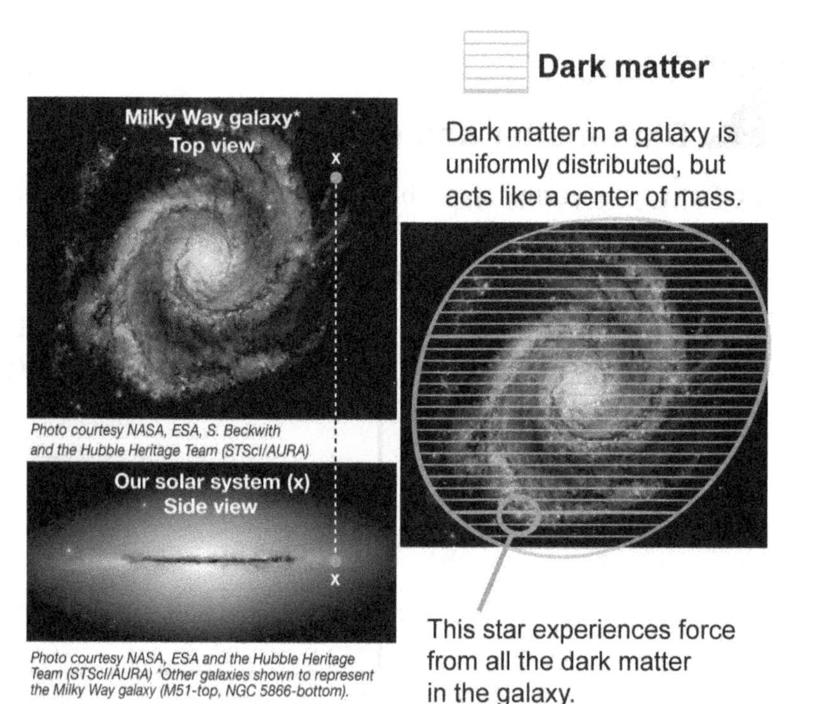

Photo courtesy NASA, ESA, S. Beckwith and the Hubble Heritage Team (STScI/AURA)

Photo courtesy NASA, ESA and the Hubble Heritage Team (STScI/AURA) *Other galaxies shown to represent the Milky Way galaxy (M51-top, NGC 5866-bottom).

Scientists are working to understand dark matter as well as dark energy, which is responsible for the accelerated expansion of the universe.

a. In the 1990s scientists believed that the expanding universe was slowing down. But, in 1998, with the aid of images from the Hubble Space Telescope, they realized that the expansion of the universe is accelerating. This newer observation led to the proposal of dark energy. According to NASA's website (http://science.nasa.gov/astrophysics/focus-areas/what-is-dark-energy/), the universe is composed of 70% dark energy, 25% dark matter, and 5% everything else (matter that we have observed). Make a pie graph to represent the composition of the universe.

b. Find a current article on the subject of dark matter or dark energy and summarize it. Hint: Conduct an Internet search for "dark matter" or "dark energy." Limit your search to news items in order to discover recent findings.

3 Computer simulations

The universe is over 13 billion years old and it began with an event called the "big bang." But modern humans (*Homo sapiens*) have only existed in Earth for hundreds of thousands of years. How have scientists figured out events that happened so long ago? How can scientists make predictions millions or billions of years into the future?

Answers to these questions are being uncovered by observing stars and galaxies using powerful telescopes and using supercomputers to generate computer models. These, computer models are then used to make videos called computer simulations. Computer models allow scientists to "see" how the universe operates on a human time scale, to test hypotheses about how the universe works, and to make predictions about the future of the universe.

To see some computer simulations go to the website of the American Museum of Natural History: www.amnh.org/sciencebulletins. Click Features or Visualizations under the heading Astro on the left hand side of the screen. Under Features, check out **Our Expanding Universe** and under Visualizations check out **Our Moon** or **Colliding Universes**.

a. Pick one of these computer simulations you viewed to summarize. Include in your summary, (1) the role of computers and other scientific tools in understanding how the universe formed, and (2) the role of gravity in how the universe changes over time.

b. The **Colliding Universes** visualization illustrates that the Milky Way is moving toward the Andromeda Galaxy. Why? What will happen when they encounter each other and when will that happen? [Source: http://www.nasa.gov/audience/forstudents/5-8/features/F_When_Gallaxies_Collide.html]

c. To create the video **Colliding Universes** the computer model included information about stars, gas, and dark matter in each galaxy. Then, the computer model evaluated how the two galaxies would respond to gravity and gas pressure over the next 6 billion years! Running the model of the collision of the two galaxies took 64 computer processors and computers working 24 hours a day for a month. Based on the information in the paragraph above, list the variables involved in the computer model. List at least two more reasons why computer models are so useful for studying the universe.

Making a Model Maglev Train

How can you make a model maglev train?

Magnetically levitating (maglev) trains do not roll on wheels. Instead, they use electromagnets to lift the train so it hovers above the tracks. Maglev technology is still in its experimental stages. However, many engineers believe that maglev trains will be used worldwide within the next 100 years.

In this investigation, you will research maglev trains and create a model maglev train.

Materials

- 30 or more magnets with north and south poles on the faces, rather than ends
- Model-building supplies such as cardboard, foam core, dowel rods, paper, tape, glue, etc.
- Materials for propelling train such as a balloon, rubber band, etc.
- Log book (notebook or stapled pages)

1 Researching maglev trains

Use the Internet to research maglev trains and find answers to the questions below. Organize your answers into an essay or create a poster.

a. What are the main parts of a maglev train?

b. How are maglev trains propelled?

c. What are the benefits of using maglev trains?

d. Where are maglev trains currently in use and where are they being built for use in the near future?

2 The engineering cycle

You will use permanent magnets to design a model maglev train of your own. Engineers design technology such as cars, computers, artificial hearts, and maglev trains. They follow a process called the engineering cycle. The parts of the cycle are:

Engineering Cycle

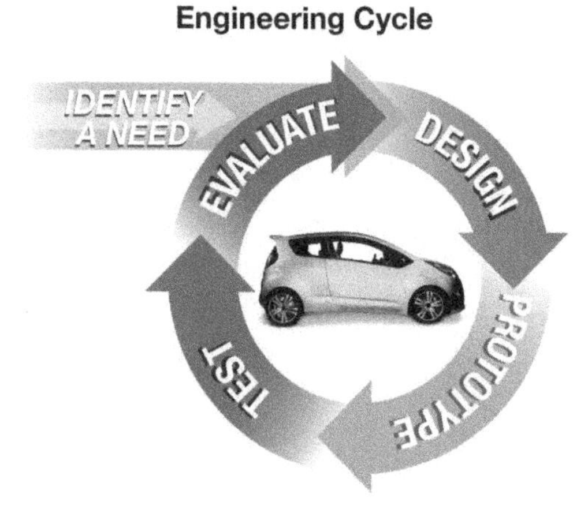

- **Identify a Need**: Define the problem and set the goal of the project. Identify the constraints and variables.
- **Design**: Brainstorm to create a list of ideas for the project. Be creative. It is okay if some ideas seem far-fetched. Do some research to refine your ideas.Then, select the best ideas. Use the ideas to create a design. Choose materials, make drawings, and decide what you will build.
- **Prototype**: Follow your design to build a prototype. Keep a record of any difficulties you have while building.
- **Test**: Find out if your prototype works. Make notes about its strengths and weaknesses.
- **Evaluate:** Once the prototype is tested, evaluate the design and brainstorm new ideas for improving it. The engineering cycle is repeated as many times as needed to create and improve products.

3 Using the engineering cycle

Keep a log book to document how you use the engineering cycle to make a model maglev train. Your log book should contain all of your notes, drawings, observations, and testing results. The guidelines below will help you work through the engineering cycle.

Identify the need

Make sure you are clear about the goals and constraints of the project. Think about how the following constraints will affect the type of maglev train model you can build.

- Your train must use permanent magnets to levitate. Use the magnets supplied by your teacher.
- Use any materials you wish for the body of the train and for the track. Common materials are cardboard, paper, plastic containers, wrapping paper rolls, and wooden dowels.
- Your train must move at least 50 cm along the track after it is released from rest.
- The propulsion device can be part of the train car, the track, or both.
- Trains will be judged on three criteria: the time it takes to travel 50 cm, design creativity, and quality of construction.

Design

1. Brainstorm ideas for your train. Make notes and sketches of how you might build the train car and the track. List possible materials you can use.
2. Brainstorm ideas for the train's propulsion. How will your train travel 50 centimeters?
3. Study your ideas. Select the best design and method of propulsion. Make a drawing of your design. Include measurements and label the materials.

Prototype

1. Build your prototype.
2. Make notes in your log book about any changes you make to the original design.

Test

Test your prototype. Make notes about what worked well and what didn't work.

Evaluate

Go back to the "design" step to improve your model. You may choose to use a completely different design, or you may want to think about ways to refine your current design. Keep going through the cycle until you have the best train you can build.

4 Comparing and evaluating models

How do your classmates' train designs compare to yours? Make comments about what you like about each design and what could be changed to make it better. Here are some guidelines to help you rate each model.

1. Watch the maglev model train in action. Record the time it takes to travel 50 centimeters.
2. Rate the train on a scale of 1 to 10 for design creativity and the quality of construction.
3. Make comments about the strong points of the design and the ways the train could be improved.

Careers in Physical Science

Chapter one introduces many of the topics you will be studying in this physical science course. These topics are important to a number of different careers. What kinds of things would a chemist do? What about a physicist? Engineers use ideas from physics and chemistry to design and create technology. Do this chapter project to learn more about a career related to physical science.

Create an Ad

Choose a career from the list. Pretend you work for a company or institution that wants to hire a qualified person for a job in this career. Design a full-page advertisement that would catch the attention of a job-seeker. Be sure the advertisement shows exactly what the person would do in the position, and what their qualifications should be. Would the new hire be helping to design a suspension bridge? Creating new tests for water quality? What education would the hire need to have? What experience should the person have? Make the advertisement accurate and attention–getting. There might be a number of qualified people for the position, but you want to convince the best person to work for your company! If you want to choose a career that is not listed, get approval from your teacher.

Career Choices

Chemist
Physicist
Electrical engineer
Mechanical engineer
Civil engineer
Chemical engineer
Biomedical engineer
Genetic engineer
Nuclear engineer
Physical therapist
Environmental scientist

Criteria for Ad	Excellent	Good	Needs some improvement	Needs much improvement	Your score
Clearly identifies the career	4	3	2	1	
Persuasive elements that grab attention	4	3	2	1	
Education and experience needed for position is accurate	4	3	2	1	
Responsibilities are reasonable and creative	4	3	2	1	
Overall appearance	4	3	2	1	
				total	

Design Your Own Experiment

Experiments are important to scientists. An experiment investigates relationships between variables in a system. In a well-designed experiment, you change only one variable at a time and keep the others constant. Do this project to design and conduct your own science experiment.

Design an Experiment

Experiments are designed to answer a question. Choose one of the questions from the list. Design and conduct an experiment to answer the question. Keep these things in mind:

- Choose a question that interests you. If you would like to write your own question, show it to your teacher.
- Write a testable hypothesis.
- Identify the variable you will be changing. Remember to keep all other variables the same throughout the experiment.
- How are you going to collect data, make measurements, and record results?
- Keep notes on your experiment so someone else could repeat it.

Be sure to show the question, hypothesis, and procedure to your teacher for approval before you begin your experiment. Follow all safety rules and ask for adult supervision. Science experiments are often conducted by groups of people since there are usually several tasks to complete at once. Prepare a report on your experiment. Photos are optional but very helpful. At the end of your report, discuss whether or not your hypothesis was confirmed.

Question Choices

1. Does a cold golf ball bounce differently than a room temperature golf ball?

2. Do objects float differently in salt water than they do in fresh water?

3. Does the material a cup or mug is made of affect the amount of time your cocoa stays warm?

4. What happens when you allow a small amount of very salty water to completely evaporate?

5. Does water temperature affect how quickly a sugar cube dissolves?

Criteria for report	Excellent	Good	Needs some improvement	Needs much improvement	Your score
Hypothesis is testable and clearly stated	4	3	2	1	
Experimental variables and controlled variables correctly chosen and identified	4	3	2	1	
Experimental procedure appropriately tests hypothesis and is described so someone else could repeat it	4	3	2	1	
Data and observations accurately collected and reported, and results linked back to hypothesis	4	3	2	1	
Overall appearance and organization	4	3	2	1	
				total	

Design a Lunar Rover

Design a Lunar Rover and win a trip to the Moon! You must submit a design for a vehicle that can carry you and three friends as you explore the surface of the Moon. The winning design will be your ticket to the Moon.

Contest Submission

Make a labeled schematic drawing of a vehicle that can carry you and three friends across the Moon's surface for day-long exploration trips.

- Draw the vehicle on a piece of poster board (or paste computer drawings on the board), show dimensions, and label important features.
- On your poster, show a specifications table that includes the vehicle's top speed in km/h, cruising speed in km/h, acceleration in km/h/s, and mass in kg.
- Label and briefly describe the device that will give energy to propel the vehicle.
- Optional: You might want to show several views of the vehicle on your poster board (top, side, front, back).

Criteria for schematic drawing	Excellent	Good	Needs some improvement	Needs much improvement	Your score
Drawing of lunar rover includes believable dimensions	4	3	2	1	
Important features labeled	4	3	2	1	
Specifications table includes all elements and values are believable	4	3	2	1	
Propulsion device labeled and described	4	3	2	1	
Overall appearance and creativity	4	3	2	1	
Bonus: more than one view of vehicle shown (1 point per additional view)					
				total	

Evaluate Designs

Present your design to others in your class that completed this project. Give feedback to others and accept feedback on your design. Some things to think about as you evaluate the designs:

1. What is the vehicle's best feature? Why is that feature well-adapted to lunar roving?

2. Is the vehicle's speed and acceleration appropriate for day-long moon trips? Why or why not?

3. How energy-efficient is the vehicle's propulsion device? Are there any drawbacks?

4. Which vehicle exhibits the most creativity?

5. Which vehicle is the most practical for the mission?

6. Which vehicle would be the most fun to travel in, and why?

Paper Aircraft Contest

Have you ever made a paper airplane? Did it fly well? Why or why not? Did you know that there are dozens and dozens, perhaps a hundred or more paper aircraft designs that people have created over the years? You can do an Internet search to see many different designs. Some paper aircraft look like airplanes, and others are more like helicopters. Some are simple to make, and others are a bit complicated. What forces allow the folded paper to stay in the air? Do this project to learn more about the physics behind paper aircraft.

Choose an Aircraft Design

Research simple paper aircraft designs. You can search the Internet, books, or interview experienced paper aircraft makers. Once you choose a design, practice making the paper aircraft and test it. Improve the design until you have the best aircraft you can make. Your aircraft should fly at least 3 meters. **If your aircraft has any sharp points, do not launch the aircraft near people. Wear eye protection such as eyeglasses or a pair of goggles.**

Fly Your Aircraft

Take your paper aircraft (and extra paper in case you need to make a duplicate) to a large open space such as a gymnasium, a classroom with tables pushed to the side, or an outside courtyard that is well-protected from the wind. **Do not launch any aircraft toward people. Wear eye protection.** Launch your aircraft five times. Each time, have a partner help you measure the total flight distance. Record these five distances. Eliminate the longest and shortest distance and average the remaining three. This will be your contest result. Next, trade roles so your partner can fly an aircraft and you can help with the distance measurements.

Share Results

Work with your classmates to make a class chart of aircraft results. How well did your aircraft fly in comparison with others? Analyze the three aircraft that flew the farthest. What aspect of each design contributed to the success? Is there anything in common between these three designs?

Analyze the Forces

Draw a free-body diagram of your aircraft. Show all forces that act on your aircraft. Your Internet or book research will help you select the forces. At the bottom of the page that shows your diagram, write a short reflection on your experience. What improvements could you make to your design to make your aircraft fly farther?

Criteria for paper aircraft	Excellent	Good	Needs some improvement	Needs much improvement	Your score
Paper aircraft carefully constructed and can fly at least 3 meters	4	3	2	1	
Completed 5 fly trials and accurately reported average distance as described above	4	3	2	1	
Free-body diagram shows all forces that act on aircraft	4	3	2	1	
Reflection paragraph clearly describes experience and includes possible design improvements	4	3	2	1	
Overall quality of project	4	3	2	1	
				total	

Sports and Newton's Laws

Newton's three laws of motion are probably the most widely used natural laws in all of science. The laws explain the relationship between forces and motion. Sports and sporting events are popular pastimes in cultures around the world. How do Newton's laws of motion apply to sports? Do this project to find out.

Choose and Describe a Sport

Choose a sport from the list below or consult your teacher if you want to work with something that is not on the list. Make notes about the sport. How is motion involved? Where is motion involved? Is speed a factor? Is accuracy important? If so, how? Describe all the aspects of the sport that involve motion.

Make a Poster

Make a poster that shows all the ways that motion is involved in your chosen sport. The poster can contain your own drawings, magazine or other printed cutouts, or a combination of visual aids. Use labeled arrows of different colors to show forces and velocities. Briefly describe how Newton's first, second, and third laws of motion are applied in the sport. Don't forget to include safety factors, if applicable.

Choices

billiards
swimming
soccer
football
gymnastics
figure skating
car racing
baseball or softball
field hockey
ice hockey
basketball
bowling
archery
volleyball
rowing
rock climbing
track and field (choose an event)
skiing
wheelchair racing
cycling

Criteria for poster	Excellent	Good	Needs some improvement	Needs much improvement	Your score
Poster shows all ways that motion is involved in the chosen sport	4	3	2	1	
Colored arrows accurately indicate forces and velocities	4	3	2	1	
Brief description of how Newton's 1st, 2nd, and 3rd laws are involved (accuracy is important)	4	3	2	1	
Applicable safety factors are included with motion elements	4	3	2	1	
Overall appearance and creativity	4	3	2	1	
				total	

Energy Transformations

A bicycle allows you to travel at faster speeds than you could on foot. In fact, the bicycle is said to be the most efficient human-powered machine for transportation. A bicycle is made up of many simple machines and moving parts that work together to transform forces from your muscles into motion. Do this project to learn more about how energy is converted from one form to another as you ride a bicycle.

Scenario

You eat dinner at 6:30 p.m. You decide to ride your bicycle to the park to meet a friend. The park is uphill from your house. It is getting dark outside. Your bike has a small electric generator that runs as the front wheel turns. You flip on the generator so that the headlight comes on as you start to pedal. You ride your bike to the park.

Note: You may change details of the scenario with your teacher's approval.

Project

Construct a diagram, flow chart, cartoon panels, mobile, or a product of your choice that shows the energy transformations that occur in the entire scenario. Don't forget to start with eating dinner. Be creative! The list of energy types below will help you identify the energy transformations. You may use the energy types once, more than once, or not at all.

- thermal energy
- chemical energy
- electrical energy
- light energy
- pressure energy
- nuclear energy
- mechanical energy

Criteria for product	Excellent	Good	Needs some improvement	Needs much improvement	Your score
Product correctly portrays scenario described above (or the one approved by your teacher)	4	3	2	1	
At least 4 energy transformations are identified	4	3	2	1	
Energy transformations are correctly labeled	4	3	2	1	
Originality of product	4	3	2	1	
Overall appearance and creativity	4	3	2	1	
				total	

Solar System Mobile

A mobile is a three-dimensional, hanging "sculpture" that can move around. Mobiles were invented by an artist named Alexander Calder (1898–1976) in the 1920s. You can make a mobile using common household materials such as a hangar, paper clips, straws, egg cartons, string, yarn, crayons, markers, cardboard, and paper.

Make a mobile

Make a mobile of the solar system. You will need: cardboard, string, scissors, tape, many colors of construction paper, colored pencils, and a compass or round objects to trace for making circles. You can follow the steps below, or make modifications as you wish.

1. Make colored circles from construction paper to represent the planets. Write the name of the planet on one side, and some interesting facts on the other side.
2. Cut out a large cardboard circle, about 40 cm in diameter. Draw the Sun in the center. Then, draw orbits around the Sun for each planet.
3. Tape string to each paper-circle planet you made in step 1. Hang each planet from the orbits you drew on the large cardboard circle. You may add comets, asteroids, and dwarf planets too.
4. Attach a string loop to the top of the cardboard circle so you can hang your mobile.

Criteria for solar system mobile	Excellent	Good	Needs some improvement	Needs much improvement	Your score
Sun, 8 planets, and orbits represented	4	3	2	1	
Planets correctly labeled and facts are included on back of each	4	3	2	1	
Mobile is well assembled and hangs correctly when attached to classroom ceiling	4	3	2	1	
Mobile is original and creative	4	3	2	1	
It is readily apparent what the mobile is supposed to represent	4	3	2	1	
Bonus: comets, asteroids, dwarf planet, or other features included (1 point per additional feature)					
				total	

Electricity and Safety

In Chapter 8 you explore electricity, electrical circuits, and the nature of electrical energy. Electricity can be powerful and dangerous. However, when you know the basic facts about how electricity works, you can use electricity safely and with confidence. Do this project to teach yourself and others about electrical safety.

CREATE A SAFETY BROCHURE

Choose a topic from the list below. Create a tri-fold brochure on important safety considerations for your chosen topic. The brochure should benefit anyone from age 10 to 100. Research your topic carefully and list your sources at the end of the brochure. Resources for information could be other consumer brochures, public utility websites, state or federal government websites, books or articles written by authors with appropriate credentials, or interviews with experts. Make your brochure informative, thorough, interesting, and eye-catching. Including facts and statistics is always helpful.

TOPICS TO CHOOSE FROM

Lightning safety

Extension cord and power strip safety

Holiday light safety (indoors and outdoors)

Light bulb safety (include types: incandescent, fluorescent, CFL, halogen)

Automobile electrical safety (include car battery)

General household electrical safety (include information about circuit breaker panel)

Criteria for brochure	Excellent	Good	Needs some improvement	Needs much improvement	Your score
Includes all important safety considerations for topic	4	3	2	1	
Appropriate for ages 10 to 100	4	3	2	1	
Resources listed at end of brochure	4	3	2	1	
Resources are credible	4	3	2	1	
Overall creativity and appearance	4	3	2	1	
				total	

Make your own Instrument

Humans were making musical instruments to produce sounds around 20,000 years before the wheel and axle were invented! Instruments gradually improved from simple flutes and drums to modern standards like the violin. Perhaps you know how to play a musical instrument. Do this project to build your own simple instrument.

Make an Instrument

There are many simple designs for instruments that can be made from materials that are easy to find. Do some research to find out how to make a simple instrument. Some ideas are: palm pipes from PVC tubing, a stringed-instrument from a shoebox and rubber bands, a straw kazoo, or bongo drums. Choose a design and build the instrument. Practice with the instrument so you can at least make different sounds, even if they are not musical. If you figure out how to play a simple recognizable tune, or rhythm, you will earn bonus points!

Explain how the instrument makes sound

Draw a diagram that explains how the instrument makes sound. Label the parts and show why each is important to the sound-making process.

Criteria for instrument project	Excellent	Good	Needs some improvement	Needs much improvement	Your score
Student can produce sounds with instrument	4	3	2	1	
Diagram correctly explains how the instrument makes sound	4	3	2	1	
Diagram contains labeled parts	4	3	2	1	
Overall creativity and appearance of instrument	4	3	2	1	
Overall clarity and appearance of diagram	4	3	2	1	
Bonus points for playing a recognizable tune or rhythm (up to 3 points possible)					
				total	

Electromagnetic Waves

The electromagnetic spectrum is a group of waves that all travel at the same speed but have different wavelengths and frequencies. The waves in this spectrum are called electromagnetic waves. You will choose a type of electromagnetic wave and create a poster and presentation to teach others about the topic. All the posters made by the class will be displayed from longest wavelength to shortest wavelength to complete a classroom spectrum.

Research a Wave

Choose a type of electromagnetic wave from the list below. Your research should include answers to the research questions listed. Do not limit yourself to these questions. Include other interesting information as well. Be sure to keep a list of all information sources.

Electromagnetic Waves to Choose From

radio waves
microwaves
infrared radiation
visible light
ultraviolet light
X-rays
gamma rays

Research Questions

1. What is the range of wavelengths for your type of wave?
2. What is the range of frequencies?
3. What is the source of the wave?
4. Who discovered this type of wave and when?
5. Are these waves easily blocked or can they pass through objects?
6. Do the waves have an effect on people? Are they harmful?
7. Discuss the uses for the waves. These may include inventions that we use in our everyday lives, medical uses, or ways scientists use the waves for research.

Make a Poster

Organize your information on a poster. Include drawings where appropriate. Make a bibliography of your sources and put it on the back of the poster.

Criteria for poster	Excellent	Good	Needs some improvement	Needs much improvement	Your score
Research questions are all addressed correctly	4	3	2	1	
Appropriate drawings or illustrations are included on poster	4	3	2	1	
Overall creativity and appearance of poster	4	3	2	1	
Bibliography is included on back of poster	4	3	2	1	
Information sources are credible	4	3	2	1	
				total	

Phase Change Story

Earth's water can exist as a solid (ice), liquid (water), or gas (water vapor or steam). What has to happen for water molecules to change from one phase to another? Do this project to show that you understand phase change processes.

WRITE A STORY

Write a creative story about a day in the life of a water molecule. You can start the water molecule in any phase you choose. The story must teach the reader what happens to water molecules when they change phases. Make sure you take the water molecule through all the phases and return to the phase you started with. Be creative when you set the scene of your story. Is this a water molecule from the ocean? From a cloud? Does the water molecule begin in a mud puddle, a frozen glacier, or perhaps in a bead of sweat on a runner's forehead? Write about how energy is involved in all of the phase changes. Illustrate your story. Feel free to create a comic strip, poem, or song if you prefer one of those over a traditional story.

Criteria for creative writing project	Excellent	Good	Needs some improvement	Needs much improvement	Your score
Writing project covers all phase changes correctly	4	3	2	1	
Project shows how energy is involved in all of the phase changes	4	3	2	1	
Illustrations help the reader understand more about phase changes	4	3	2	1	
Originality	4	3	2	1	
Overall creativity and appearance	4	3	2	1	
				total	

Extraordinary Materials

Materials scientists study the properties of different materials. They design, create, and discover new materials to meet the demands of rapidly changing industries. Do this project to learn more about an extraordinary material of your choice.

Choose a Material

Many materials have been discovered, developed, and invented that could be described as extraordinary. Choose a material from the list below. If you would like to learn about a material that is not on the list, ask your teacher.

- Vulcanized rubber
- Carbon nanotubes
- Memory wire
- Aerogel
- Kevlar
- Spider silk

Make a Poster

Create a poster for your chosen material. Provide a drawing, representation, illustration, or photo of the material. Include answers to these questions:

1. Does the material occur naturally, or is it synthetic? When was it first discovered or invented? By what group or person?
2. What are the most important properties of this material?
3. What are some uses for this material?
4. Include on your poster your own idea for how this material could be used in the future.

Criteria for poster	Excellent	Good	Needs some improvement	Needs much improvement	Your score
Material is represented by a drawing, illustration, or photo	4	3	2	1	
Relevant information (#1–3 above)	4	3	2	1	
Poster shows your own idea for how this material could be used in the future	4	3	2	1	
Accuracy of information	4	3	2	1	
Overall creativity and appearance	4	3	2	1	
				total	

Atomic Model

Atoms are made up of three basic particles: protons, neutrons, and electrons. In this project you will construct a three-dimensional model of an atom in the style of what is called a "Bohr atom". Neils Bohr was a Danish physicist. He proposed that electrons occupy discrete energy levels outside the nucleus.

Create a Three-Dimensional Atom Model

Choose an atom from the list below. Make a three-dimensional model of the atoms's structure, using the Bohr model. Choose different materials to represent protons, neutrons, and electrons. Make a small poster with a key to show what each material represents. Also, include at least three interesting facts about the atom. Put the name of the atom on the *back* of the poster. This way, when you see your classmate's projects, you can guess which atom they modeled and then check to see if you are correct.

Atoms to Choose From

helium	beryllium	carbon	oxygen
lithium	boron	nitrogen	neon

Criteria for atom model	Excellent	Good	Needs some improvement	Needs much improvement	Your score
Model has correct number of protons, neutrons, and electrons	4	3	2	1	
Model has protons, neutrons, and electrons in correct locations	4	3	2	1	
Poster has a key to show what each material represents	4	3	2	1	
Poster has 3 interesting facts about the atom on the front of the poster and the name of the atom on the back	4	3	2	1	
Overall creativity and appearance	4	3	2	1	
				total	

Element Game

Elements are the building blocks for vast numbers of molecules and compounds we encounter each day. The elements are arranged on the periodic table. Elements like helium (He) and oxygen (O) might be familiar to you. What about sodium (Na)? Why is the symbol "Na" instead of "S"? Create a game to help you and your classmates become more familiar with element names, symbols, and atomic numbers.

Develop and Make a Game

Create an element game that you and three classmates can play. The object of the game is to help the players become more familiar with the name, symbol, and atomic number of elements 1–18. Your game should have an instruction sheet with the objective, rules, and how to win the game. If your game requires cards or a game board and pieces, you must create or provide those. If you create a computer game, you must turn in a disk or flash drive with the file. Be sure to create the game in an application that your classroom computers or computer lab already has installed.

Criteria for element game	Excellent	Good	Needs some improvement	Needs much improvement	Your score
Game objective is clearly stated	4	3	2	1	
Rules support the objective and are easy to understand	4	3	2	1	
Game materials or computer file have been created so classmates can play the game	4	3	2	1	
Game actually works and helps players learn the names, symbols, and atomic numbers of elements 1 - 19	4	3	2	1	
Overall creativity and quality	4	3	2	1	
				total	

Compound Hall of Fame

Most matter exists as compounds, not pure elements. Chemical compounds are all around us. Some compounds exist in the world naturally, and others are made in laboratories for lots of different purposes. New chemical compounds are being made and introduced at a steady rate. Chemical compounds are used to sweeten food, control insects, make clothes stretchy, straighten hair, and treat diseases, among a multitude of other uses. Of all the new chemical compounds invented or developed since 1950, which ones should make it into the "Compound Hall of Fame"?

Research new chemical compounds

Do some research to learn the names and uses of some chemical compounds that have been invented or developed since 1950. You will learn about chemicals used for pest control, improving growing conditions, food additives, medicines, clothing fibers, and cosmetics, among many others. Pick one chemical compound that you would like to nominate for acceptance into the "Compound Hall of Fame."

Write and give a nomination speech

Write a persuasive speech on behalf of your nominated compound. You must convince the selection committee to include your compound in the Compound Hall of Fame. One compound out of all the nominations will win the top prize: "Best Chemical Compound of All Time." The speech should be about two to three minutes long. Include a poster with your speech that has the following items:

- Scientific name of chemical compound, common name, and chemical formula
- Who discovered or developed the compound, and when
- Uses of the compound
- Pros and cons of the compound
- Main reason why you nominated the compound

Criteria for project	Excellent	Good	Needs some improvement	Needs much improvement	Your score
Nominated compound was invented or developed between 1950 and the present	4	3	2	1	
Overall quality of persuasive speech	4	3	2	1	
Poster contains items listed above	4	3	2	1	
Overall quality of poster	4	3	2	1	
Score from nominating committee (if your compound is selected "all-time best", you will receive a 4 here. All others will receive a 3, 2, or 1).	4	3	2	1	
				total	

pH Scale Mobile

Acids and bases are familiar compounds. Vinegar is a common acid, and ammonia is an ordinary base. The pH scale is used to describe whether a substance has acidic or basic properties. Do the project to create a visual pH scale that shows substances in place of pH values.

Make a Mobile

Create a pH scale mobile. The scale can be displayed horizontally or vertically, from low pH to high pH. In place of pH values, hang an illustration, drawing, photo, or actual product label of a substance that matches the pH range. The seven pH ranges to represent are: 0–2, 3–4, 5–6, 7, 8–9, 10–11, and 12–14. Use color to enhance the scale effect, to match what a universal pH indicator would show for each pH range.

Criteria for mobile	Excellent	Good	Needs some improvement	Needs much improvement	Your score
Mobile represents all seven pH ranges specified above	4	3	2	1	
Substances used to represent pH ranges are correct	4	3	2	1	
Mobile hangs so the scale is in order from low pH to high pH	4	3	2	1	
Correct use of color to enhance the scale ranges	4	3	2	1	
Overall quality and appearance of mobile	4	3	2	1	
				total	

Model a Chemical Reaction

If you leave a tarnished copper penny in acid for a few minutes the penny becomes shiny again. The copper oxide that tarnished the penny was removed by a chemical reaction with the acid. Chemical reactions are the process through which chemical changes occur. Do this project to learn more about a chemical reaction of your choice.

Choose a Chemical Reaction

Do some research on a variety of common chemical reactions. Choose a chemical reaction that interests you. Make notes on what the reactants and products are. Be sure you have the correct balanced chemical equation for the reaction.

Create a Three-Dimensional Model

Make a three-dimensional model of the chemical reaction. It can stand on its own or be mounted to poster board, a box lid, or some other surface or stand. All atoms must be represented. No numerals allowed! You are modeling the atoms involved in the reaction. Attach a small poster to the model, or display the poster to one side. On the front of the poster, create a key that shows what the atoms in the model are. Write a balanced equation for the chemical reaction on the *back* of the poster. This way, others can study your model, try to write the balanced equation, and then check their work.

Criteria for model	Excellent	Good	Needs some improvement	Needs much improvement	Your score
Chemical equation is correct and appears on the back of small poster	4	3	2	1	
Reactants are correctly represented in the 3-D model	4	3	2	1	
Products are correctly represented in the 3-D model	4	3	2	1	
A key on the small poster identifies the atoms involved in the reaction	4	3	2	1	
Overall creativity and appearance	4	3	2	1	
				total	